D1096168

The Round World

MICHAEL DEMPSEY, B.A.

FOUNDATIONS OF SCIENCE LIBRARY

GREYSTONE PRESS/NEW YORK · TORONTO · LONDON

Contents

THE NATURE OF THE EARTH . . . . . *page* 5

  1 THE STRUCTURE OF THE EARTH 6

  2 DRILLING THROUGH THE EARTH'S CRUST . . 11

  3 READING THE ROCKS 14

  4 THE WORK OF THE GEOLOGIST 21

THE SKIN OF THE EARTH 27

  5 SEDIMENTARY ROCKS 28

  6 LIMESTONES 32

  7 IGNEOUS AND METAMORPHIC ROCKS . . . 34

  8 FOLDS AND FAULTS 38

  9 SOILS 41

THE RESTLESS EARTH 47

  10 VOLCANIC ERUPTIONS 49

  11 EARTHQUAKES 51

  12 HOW MOUNTAINS ARE MADE 54

  13 CONTINENTAL DRIFT 58

The Round World

MICHAEL DEMPSEY, B.A.

FOUNDATIONS OF SCIENCE LIBRARY

GREYSTONE PRESS/NEW YORK · TORONTO · LONDON

CHIEF EDITORS

Leslie Basford, B.Sc.   Philip Kogan, M.Sc.

ASSISTANT EDITORS

Michael Dempsey, B.A., Michael Gabb, B.Sc., Clare Dover, B.Sc.
Cyril Parsons, B.Sc., Joan Pick, B.Sc., Michael Chinery, B.A.
David Larkin, B.Sc., Paul Drury Byrne, B.Sc.

CONSULTANT EDITORIAL BOARD

Sir Lawrence Bragg, M.C., O.B.E., F.R.S., M.A., Nobel Laureate
Sir James Chadwick, F.R.S., Ph.D., M.Sc., Nobel Laureate
Norman Fisher, M.A.
Sir Harry Melville, K.C.B., F.R.S., Ph.D., D.Sc.
Professor J. Z. Young, F.R.S., M.A.

This new presentation assembles freshly edited material from
'Understanding Science' on one subject into a single volume.

Copyright © MCMLXVI Sampson Low, Marston & Co. Ltd.

Library of Congress Catalog Card Number: 66–17989

Printed in Great Britain
Manufactured in U.S.A.

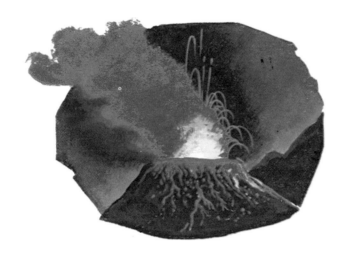

Contents

THE NATURE OF THE EARTH . . . . . *page* 5

  1 THE STRUCTURE OF THE EARTH 6

  2 DRILLING THROUGH THE EARTH'S CRUST . . 11

  3 READING THE ROCKS 14

  4 THE WORK OF THE GEOLOGIST 21

THE SKIN OF THE EARTH 27

  5 SEDIMENTARY ROCKS 28

  6 LIMESTONES 32

  7 IGNEOUS AND METAMORPHIC ROCKS . . . 34

  8 FOLDS AND FAULTS 38

  9 SOILS 41

THE RESTLESS EARTH 47

  10 VOLCANIC ERUPTIONS 49

  11 EARTHQUAKES 51

  12 HOW MOUNTAINS ARE MADE . . . 54

  13 CONTINENTAL DRIFT 58

The Shaping of the Land .   .   .   .   .   *page* 65

14   Weathering   66

15   The Agents of Erosion   .   .   .   70

16   The Work of Rivers.   73

17   The Work of Ice   79

18   The Work of the Wind   .   .   .   83

19   The Work of the Sea   85

20   How Caves are Formed   .   .   .   91

The Wealth of the Earth.   95

21   Oil Geology   96

22   Fuel from Ancient Forests   .   .   .   100

23   Natural Gas   104

24   Heat from the Earth   106

25   Where Metals Come From   .   .   .   112

26   Identifying Minerals.   116

27   Commercially Important Minerals   .   .   121

Index   127

The Nature
of the Earth

CHAPTER ONE

The Structure of the Earth

A CERTAIN amount can be learnt about the structure of the Earth from a study of the surface rocks. Sedimentary rocks include those which have been laid down beneath shallow seas and later raised above the waves by earth movements, or exposed by a fall in sea-level. These are made up of mud, sand and bits of older rock, carried down by river, or of animal and plant remains. Rocks like these cover a large part of the continents and mask the true nature of the land masses. The rocks that cover the British Isles, for instance, are of all geological ages and suggest that it has been repeatedly submerged beneath shallow seas. There are, however, parts of the land areas which have not been submerged for millions of years. In these places water, wind and ice have stripped off any sedimentary rock covering, exposing the heart rock of the continents—granite. Since the minerals of which granites and related rocks are composed are made up mainly of the oxides of two elements, silicon and aluminium, the material of the continental masses has been given the name *sial* (*Si* is the chemical symbol for silicon and *Al* the symbol for aluminium). The average density of sial is about 2·7 grams per cubic centimetre, but it is known that the average density of the Earth as a whole is 5·5 (this can be calculated from the volume of the Earth and the force of gravity). So it is clear that much denser material must lie beneath the sial.

The ocean floor is quite different from the continents. The continental shelf which extends some distance out to sea is really part of the continents. At deeper levels, however, the ocean floor is covered with *oozes* made up from the skeletons of various minute sea creatures. At any great depth even these skeletons dissolve, and in the deepest ocean basins the only covering is a relatively thin layer of red clay, made up mainly of volcanic dust and cosmic dust from outer space together with virtually insoluble materials such as shark's teeth. The red colouring is due to ferric oxide (an iron compound) in the volcanic dust. Samples brought up from these great depths have shown that beneath the red clay lies basalt, a rock formed, like granite, from cooling molten matter. The fact that most volcanic oceanic islands have been built up of ejected basalt or related rocks is further evidence for believing that basalt forms the Earth's crust beneath the oceans. And since great flows of basalt have welled up through fissures in the land masses in the past (e.g. the Deccan Traps of India) it is fairly certain that this basaltic layer is 'universal', i.e. it extends beneath the continents too. This is reasonable since basalt is denser than granite (2.95 compared to 2·7). The basaltic layer has been given the name *sima*, for its minerals are composed mainly of oxides of silicon and magnesium (*Si* is the symbol for silicon and *Ma* an abbreviation, though not the chemical symbol, for magnesium). Thus it is possible to

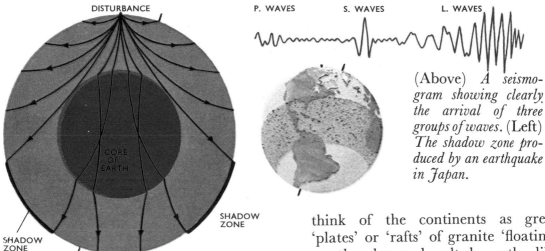

DISTURBANCE

P. WAVES   S. WAVES   L. WAVES

CORE
OF
EARTH

SHADOW
ZONE

SHADOW
ZONE

(Above) *A seismo-gram showing clearly the arrival of three groups of waves.* (Left) *The shadow zone produced by an earthquake in Japan.*

For every earthquake there is a shadow zone round the world where primary waves are not received. The reason is that those waves which strike the Earth's core are sharply refracted due to the sudden change in density, while those that just miss the core travel on as normal. This produces a large gap in the waves reaching the surface and has helped to prove the existence of a central core of very dense material.

think of the continents as great 'plates' or 'rafts' of granite 'floating' on the denser basalt beneath, like ice-floes float on water.

Until recently the deeper levels of the Earth were a complete mystery. Some people believed the thin, wrinkled crust to enclose a vast mass of molten rock, while others considered the centre of the Earth to be an inferno of gases. It was only with the application of seismology (the scientific study of earthquakes) to the problem that speculation gave way to scientific reasoning.

A *fault* in geology is a fracture in the Earth's crust along which the rocks have moved in relation to each other. When faulting occurs and the moving rocks rub against each other, vibrations spread out in all directions producing an earthquake. Most earthquakes are produced in this way, though some are associated with volcanic activity. Near the disturbance the ground itself can be felt shaking (it is sometimes possible to *see* it shaking), but the tremors die down with distance until it is only possible to detect them with a delicate instrument called a seismograph.

There are three groups of 'quake' waves, each of which is transmitted in a different way. Primary waves ('push and pull' waves) are waves of

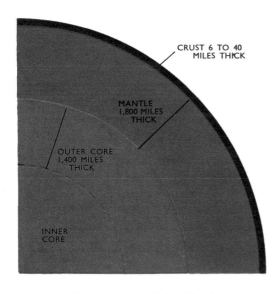

CRUST 6 TO 40
MILES THICK

MANTLE
1,800 MILES
THICK

OUTER CORE
1,400 MILES
THICK

INNER
CORE

The structure of the Earth.

compression, similar to those of sound, where each particle of rock vibrates in the direction of the ray (the path followed by the waves). Secondary waves are waves of distortion ('shake' waves) in which each particle vibrates at right angles to the direction of the ray. Long waves are confined to the Earth's crust by reflection from its upper and lower limits. Primary waves are the fastest and long waves the slowest. If a recording station is far enough away from the centre of the disturbance the seismographic

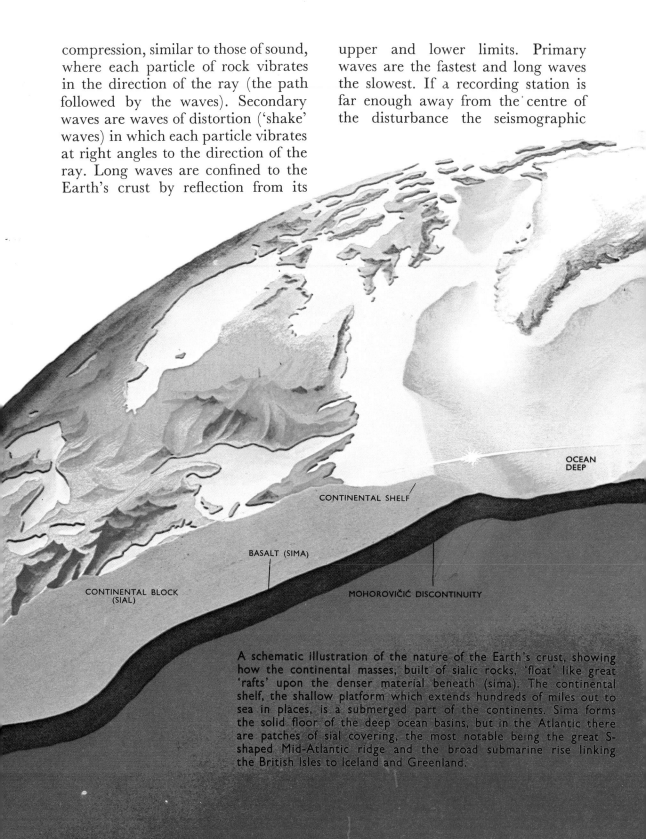

OCEAN
DEEP

CONTINENTAL SHELF

BASALT (SIMA)

CONTINENTAL BLOCK
(SIAL)

MOHOROVIČIĆ DISCONTINUITY

A schematic illustration of the nature of the Earth's crust, showing how the continental masses, built of sialic rocks, 'float' like great 'rafts' upon the denser material beneath (sima). The continental shelf, the shallow platform which extends hundreds of miles out to sea in places, is a submerged part of the continents. Sima forms the solid floor of the deep ocean basins, but in the Atlantic there are patches of sial covering, the most notable being the great S-shaped Mid-Atlantic ridge and the broad submarine rise linking the British Isles to Iceland and Greenland.

record (seismogram) shows three definite pulses as the three groups arrive one after another.

The value of seismograms lies in the fact that the velocity of primary and secondary waves depends upon the density of the material through which they travel and its resistance to compression (in the case of primary waves) or distortion (in the case of secondary waves). So once their source and the time they have taken to cover the journey to the recording station has been determined (this is

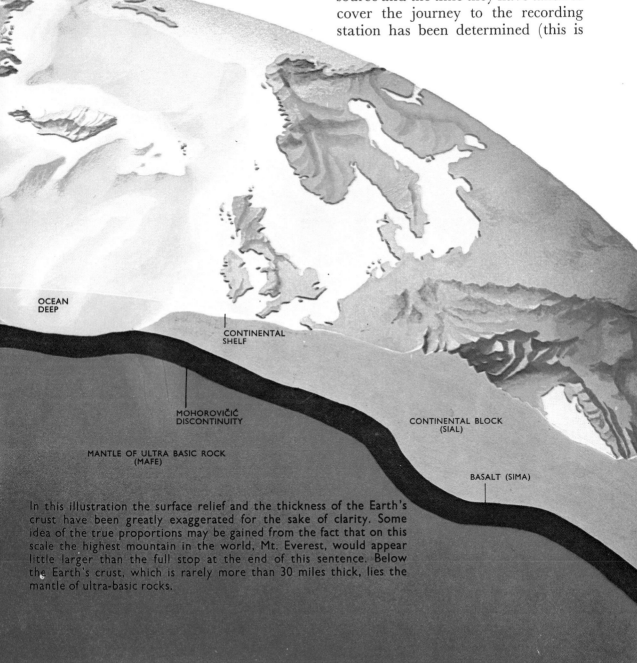

OCEAN DEEP

CONTINENTAL SHELF

MOHOROVIČIĆ DISCONTINUITY

CONTINENTAL BLOCK (SIAL)

MANTLE OF ULTRA BASIC ROCK (MAFE)

BASALT (SIMA)

In this illustration the surface relief and the thickness of the Earth's crust have been greatly exaggerated for the sake of clarity. Some idea of the true proportions may be gained from the fact that on this scale the highest mountain in the world, Mt. Everest, would appear little larger than the full stop at the end of this sentence. Below the Earth's crust, which is rarely more than 30 miles thick, lies the mantle of ultra-basic rocks.

shown by the interval between the arrival of the primary and secondary waves) the density of the materials through which they have passed can be calculated. The difficulty here is that the density of a material cannot be directly translated into *chemical composition*; a certain density can only *correspond* to a certain composition.

The very fact that long waves are reflected from the lower limit of the Earth's crust shows that it must be different in composition from the material below. They also show that it has a well-defined base lying at a depth of about 22 miles beneath the average land surface and only four miles beneath the ocean floor. This was discovered by the Yugoslavian seismologist Mohorovičić; hence it is known as the Mohorovičić discontinuity (and often referred to as the 'Moho' for obvious reasons). The speed of quake waves through the crust confirms the composition suggested by the surface rocks.

The speed of quake waves which pass beneath the Moho suggests that there is a layer of ultra-basic rocks (very dense rocks) possibly very similar in composition to *peridotite*. The minerals of this rock are composed mainly of oxides of magnesium and iron, hence the layer is referred to by some as the *mafe*. Ultra-basic rock forms the *mantle* of the Earth and extends to a depth of about 1,800 miles. But heavy as the ultra-basic rocks are they cannot by sheer 'packing' reach even the average density of the Earth (5·5), so somewhere there is some very heavy material indeed.

At a depth of 1,800 miles seismic waves undergo a sudden acceleration and show that there is a jump in density far more striking than that at the Moho (from about 5·7 to 9·7).

This marks the boundary of the Earth's core in which the density continues to increase until a maximum of 12·3 is reached at the centre.

The material making up the core of the Earth is thought to consist mainly of iron with some nickel and chromium. This composition not only satisfies seismic requirements but ties in with other evidence. The abundance of iron oxide in the crustal rocks, for instance, suggests that there is a great deal of pure iron at lower levels, and meteorites, which are part of the solar system and therefore formed from the same materials as the Earth, are often composed of iron with smaller amounts of nickel and cobalt.

Liquid or Solid

The state of the materials lying beneath the Earth's crust is hard to imagine. Measurements have shown that the temperature below ground increases at a rate of 1°F. for every 60 feet of depth (1°C. for every 108 feet). This means that rocks should be in a molten state below 30 miles, a fact which is borne out by the molten lava of volcanoes. But this rate of increase of temperature does not continue unchecked to the centre of the Earth; it tails off so that the maximum temperature reached is probably around 6,000°C. at the centre of the core.

Seismic waves are also of use in determining the state of the hidden rocks, especially the secondary or 'shake' waves. These waves will not travel through liquids yet they *will* travel through the mantle of the Earth, so clearly it must be at least in a pseudo-solid state. But 'shake' waves do *not* travel through the Earth's core. Hence the core, or at least its outer part, must be in some kind of molten condition. This idea is borne out by the nature of 'rock tides' (the Moon not only causes tides of water on the Earth but also tides in the solid rock, though the amount of movement is exceedingly small). The way in which primary waves accelerate when passing through the core suggests that there is an inner core which is not molten but rigid.

Thus the picture of the world according to present belief shows a thin crust, rarely more than 30 miles thick, overlying a mantle of solid ultra-basic rock extending down to a depth of 1,800 miles. Below this lies the Earth's core, composed mainly of iron, molten for the first 1,400 miles, then solid to the centre of the Earth.

CHAPTER TWO

Drilling through the Earth's Crust

THOUGH geologists are certain that the rock lying beneath the crust of the Earth is very dense, they have been unable so far to gain any definite evidence about its mineral content. Recently a team of American scientists explored the oceans with a view to sinking a bore-hole right through the crust, across the Mohorovičić discontinuity which marks its base, and into the mantle. The proposed borehole and all that goes with it is called the Mohole. Unfortunately, the scheme has so far proved too expensive to be completed.

The Mohole

The aim of the Mohole project is to drill a hole three miles through the Earth's crust and bring up samples of the mantle beneath. Since the mantle has never been examined before, this would be a landmark in the history of geology. Clearly the best place to drill the Mohole is where the crust is thinner than average, that is, under the ocean. On land the deepest drilling possible by present methods is estimated at about 10 miles. And the Moho is 20 miles below the surface. Furthermore, drilling on land is limited by the high temperatures existing at depth. Measurements of heat flow out of the crust indicate that the crust may reach a temperature of 500°C at a depth of 10 miles. Under the ocean, temperatures of no more than 200°C are expected.

Of five possible sites, two were chosen for trials. They were selected on the basis of seismic surveys to trace the Moho, geological surveys, and

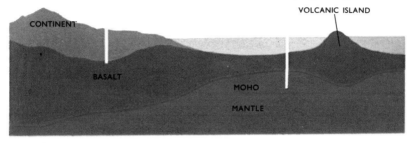

This section through the crust shows how the Moho gets deeper under the continents.

measurements of the Earth's gravity. Account was also taken of prevailing winds and ocean currents. The availability of a suitable, not too distant port was also an important consideration. In 1961, holes were drilled into the ocean floor from CUSS I, a floating drilling platform.

The first site lay in the Pacific Ocean, in the San Diego Trench, off La Jolla, California. The trials carried out at this site gave valuable information on drilling techniques in deep water. Five holes were drilled under 3,111 feet of water. The deepest hole was sunk 1,035 feet below the ocean floor. Samples of sediment were obtained and used to date periods in the last few hundred million years of the Earth's history. The sediment is a mud-like material of clay, silt and the fossil shells of animals and plants. It is easy to drill through, and the fossils give valuable clues for dating purposes.

The second site was near Guadalupe Island, off the Mexican coast of the Pacific Ocean. Five holes were drilled under 11,700 feet of water. The deepest hole went down 600 feet into the ocean bed. It penetrated about 44 feet of *basalt*. The crust under the ocean is made of a layer of hard basalt rock which is covered by a layer of sediment. This was the first time that the basalt layer had ever been sampled *in situ*. From samples of the rock, its composition was found to be similar to that of the basalt from various Haw-

aiian volcanoes. Samples taken from the sediment at a depth of 350 feet below the ocean floor contained fossils about 20 million years old. By comparison, radioactive dating of the oldest known rocks gave them an age of 2,700 million years.

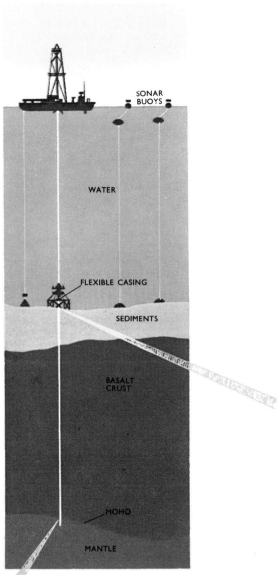

A typical drilling bit studded with diamond.

A drawing to show the relative thicknesses of water, sediments and basalts through which the drill must pass on its way to the Moho. The drilling bit and flexible casing are shown in greater detail.

Two other sites have also been investigated: off Puerto Rico and on St. Paul's Rock in the south Atlantic Ocean, 600 miles off Brazil.

Drilling Methods

The methods of drilling used on the Mohole project are similar to those used for drilling off-shore oil wells. But, because the water is much deeper than over off-shore wells, new techniques were required. The first problem was to keep the ship positioned over the drilling hole. The water is too deep for anchoring the ship. Four anchors, each with chains $3\frac{1}{2}$ miles long, would have been needed, and would clearly have been out of the question. Another method considered was to use a strong pipe thick enough both to do the drilling and at the same time to moor the ship. When the pipe was still, the slow deep ocean currents would cause little bending. But when it rotated at high speed a large pressure would be built up on one side of the pipe. This build up is known as the *Magnus Effect*, and is the reason why a ball swerves when it is spinning rapidly.

The best answer seemed to be for the ship to be fitted with four swivelling motors, two on each side, fore and aft, to keep the ship over the hole. Thus, if a wind or current carried the ship

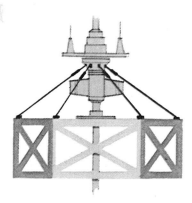

to port (left), the port motors would be angled across the length of the ship, and would drive it back again to starboard (right). To know when the ship was off position a ring of buoys was fixed on taut wires to the seabed. Six lens-shaped aluminium buoys were moored securely, submerged about 200 feet under the surface of the sea, by steel wires. Attached to the buoys were *sonar* (*so*und *n*avigation *a*nd *r*ange) devices which reflected high frequency sound waves for determining the ship's position relative to the buoys. Attached to each submerged buoy by a wire and floating on the surface were radar reflectors which showed the position of the ship on a radar screen. The four outboard motors, each 200 h.p., were coupled so that the ship could be moved round in any direction at the touch of a joy-stick, and by observing the position indicated by the instruments, the pilot could hold the ship within 200 feet of a point directly over the hole.

Even with the ship accurately positioned, the two-mile-long steel drill pipe was as flexible as a thin wire hanging from the top of a tall building. The drill pipe was connected to the turning machinery on board a barge. The lower end of the pipe was held on the ocean floor by a heavy *drill collar*, which acted much like a sinker on a fishing line. To prevent the pipe's bending too much at the top end, it passed through a conical hole, called a *guide shoe*. At the lower end of the pipe a *flexible casing*, like a lobster pot, was used. The drilling bits were made of tungsten carbide studded with diamonds, and were about 9 inches across. Core samples could be drawn up through the centre of the bit. Once the drill pipe is withdrawn from a hole it is impossible to locate the hole again. Therefore, when the Mohole proper is finally drilled, a *riser pipe* going from the hole almost to the surface of the sea will be installed.

The ship will thus be able to leave the drilling site when necessary. On return, it will find the riser pipe, buoyed up by floats, and feed the drill pipe down to the hole.

Aims

If ever completed, the Mohole project will show whether the Moho is a sharp boundary or a zone of gradual change. It will give a better clue to the age of the Earth's crust, and of the mantle inside. Core samples will throw light on not only the age of the oceans but of life itself on Earth. The Mohole will tell us what the ocean crust is made of. Its composition can then be compared with that of meteorites from outer space, to see if there is a common origin to both. Instruments left in the Mohole will give information on the source of the Earth's heat, whether from nuclear fission or not, and of the Earth's residual magnetism. The latter information may prove how the continents were formed, and may uphold or disprove the theory of *continental drift*. The Mohole project when completed should thus provide valuable information for a number of branches of science.

CHAPTER THREE

Reading the Rocks

EVER since the Earth's formation, its surface has been subjected to erosion, deposition, folding and uplift. The story of all these changes is written in the rocks and its unravelling is part of the science of geology. One of the basic principles involved was first put forward in 1785 by a Scottish geologist named James Hutton. He had watched cliffs crumbling and sand being carried out to sea and he realised that here were new rocks in the making. He reasoned that such changes had been going on for millions of years and that the same processes that form rocks today must have formed similar rocks long ago. This idea, that *'the present is the key to the past'*, is very simple, but at the time was quite new.

The value of Hutton's ideas, which were published in 1795 in his 'Theory

An unconformity. The lower, older rocks had been folded and eroded for long periods before the upper ones were laid down. The irregular junction thus represents the passage of many millions of years.

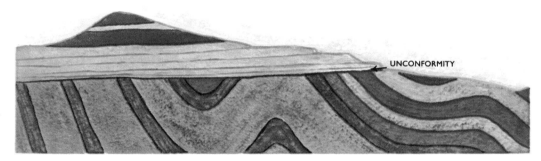

UNCONFORMITY

14

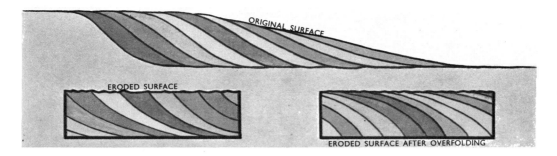

ORIGINAL SURFACE

ERODED SURFACE

ERODED SURFACE AFTER OVERFOLDING

When material is deposited at the edge of a lake or just off-shore, it settles in a typical curve. Subsequent erosion of the material leaves a truncated surface and it is obvious which was the top, even if the beds have since been turned upside down by overfolding.

of the Earth' were not realised for some time but they are now the basis of *palaeogeography*. Coal-seams, limestones and conglomerates all indicate certain past conditions and by following them we can deduce the geography at the time of their formation. Hutton was also the first person to explain and understand *unconformities* – junctions where one rock layer rests on irregular surfaces of one or more older layers. Hutton correctly assumed that the lower rocks had been subjected to erosion before the upper layer was deposited; in other words, there was a break in the geological column at that place. Such breaks may represent millions of years of erosion.

Another famous geologist who helped to unravel the story of the rocks was William Smith – the 'Father of English Geology'. He had collected fossils as a child and continued to do so during his career as a surveyor. Road and canal construction gave him ample opportunity to study the rocks and their fossils. As a result of his studies, Smith stated the **Law of Superposition** – '*Of any two rock formations, that which was originally the lower, is the older of the two*'. This idea had been put forward earlier when it was realised that sedimentary rocks

are made up of deposited fragments. William Smith also produced another law relating to fossils. He realised that '*each group or series of rocks has a characteristic collection of fossils that do not appear either above or below the rocks in question*'. Using this law it is thus possible to place any rock formation in its right place in the geological column.

Fossils are extremely important to the student of geology, but not all fossils are of value in dating rocks. The most valuable ones are those of animals that evolved and spread rapidly and then disappeared. Such fossils as the graptolites are ideal and can be used to date a rock quite accurately. Animals (and plants) that continued unchanged for a long time and those that occurred in only a small area are of no value for comparing the ages of rocks.

The work of Hutton and Smith therefore laid the foundations of *stratigraphy*. This is the branch of science that deals with the geography of geological periods and the way in which the records are preserved in the rocks. For example, by applying the work of these two men to the rocks of a particular area we can deduce its history. The fossils tell us the relative ages of the rocks, and whether they are marine, fresh-water or land deposits, and also something of the climate. Hutton showed how we can follow the formation of the rocks and the changes that have taken place since.

The younger rocks of Britain occur mainly in the south and east and it is quite easy to follow the succession. Further north, however, the rocks have been greatly disturbed and folded and many of them occur only in isolated patches. Where fossils occur it is easy to place the rocks in their right position but, quite often, fossils are absent and other methods must be used.

The nature of the rock itself can sometimes be used to correlate it. If two outcrops contain the same sorts of pebbles and minerals it is likely that they are parts of the same deposit but a feature known as *diachronism* (= across time) can upset this reasoning. If pebbles or sands are being deposited in a slowly sinking region the beds formed, although continuous, will cut across the time-scale at the edges. If fossils are present they may be of very different types and indicate a great difference in age. *Lithology* (the study of the nature of rocks) is not, therefore a reliable guide on its own.

Many rocks contain very distinctive minerals or groups of minerals. If pebbles of such a rock occur in other rocks, the latter must obviously be younger. If this younger rock contains fossils, a minimum age in the geological time scale can be obtained for that particular rock. If it overlies fossiliferous rocks, a maximum age can be obtained too. It is necessary to ensure that the rocks are the right way up, however, for it is possible that *overfolds* might have occurred so that the older rocks now lie on top.

Several features help to show if a rock is the right way up. *Cross-bedding* or *current-bedding* of sands deposited on land or in water can be important. It gives a characteristic curve to the layers and if part is later eroded it is clear which was the top and bottom. Ripple-marks and sun-cracks in sand and mud can fill up with sand before being smoothed out, and again, it is obvious which rock was underneath. Water-borne deposits show *graded bedding* – the coarser particles coming down first, followed by finer ones. Where sediment was supplied only periodically, the successive layers clearly show top and bottom. The older of two rocks can also be determined by finding derived pebbles in the other one.

The early geologists believed that granites and other igneous rocks were

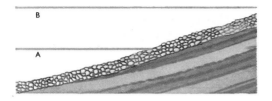

In appearance, the gravel deposit looks the same all through, but the right-hand end is much younger than the left because sea-level gradually rose from A to B. This feature of a rock cutting across the time zones, is called diachronism.

Folds can overturn rock layers but fossils indicate the correct succession.

formed before all the sedimentary rocks, but James Hutton disproved this by finding dykes of igneous rocks cutting across sediments. As they lack fossils, igneous rocks are also difficult to date. Obviously they must be younger than the sediments that they cut across and older than the sediments deposited on their worn surfaces, but intrusions that did not reach the surface are more difficult to date. A maximum age can be given but not a minimum. The igneous rocks are hot when they invade the sediments and the latter are usually altered by the

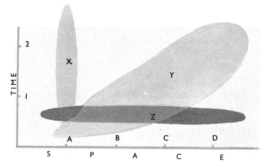

The distribution of fossils in time and space. Fossil X is useless for dating rocks as it occurs over a long period of time in a restricted area. Fossil Y is also no good as it covers a long period of time. Fossil Z is very good. It is widespread and confined to a short period of time.

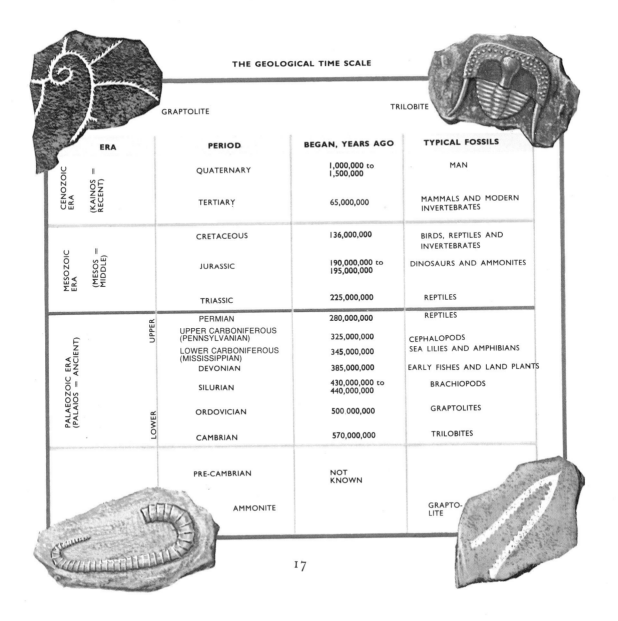

THE GEOLOGICAL TIME SCALE

GRAPHOLITE

TRILOBITE

ERA		PERIOD	BEGAN, YEARS AGO	TYPICAL FOSSILS
CENOZOIC ERA (KAINOS = RECENT)		QUATERNARY	1,000,000 to 1,500,000	MAN
		TERTIARY	65,000,000	MAMMALS AND MODERN INVERTEBRATES
MESOZOIC ERA (MESOS = MIDDLE)		CRETACEOUS	136,000,000	BIRDS, REPTILES AND INVERTEBRATES
		JURASSIC	190,000,000 to 195,000,000	DINOSAURS AND AMMONITES
		TRIASSIC	225,000,000	REPTILES
PALAEOZOIC ERA (PALAIOS = ANCIENT)	UPPER	PERMIAN	280,000,000	REPTILES
		UPPER CARBONIFEROUS (PENNSYLVANIAN)	325,000,000	CEPHALOPODS
		LOWER CARBONIFEROUS (MISSISSIPPIAN)	345,000,000	SEA LILIES AND AMPHIBIANS
		DEVONIAN	385,000,000	EARLY FISHES AND LAND PLANTS
	LOWER	SILURIAN	430,000,000 to 440,000,000	BRACHIOPODS
		ORDOVICIAN	500,000,000	GRAPTOLITES
		CAMBRIAN	570,000,000	TRILOBITES
		PRE-CAMBRIAN	NOT KNOWN	

AMMONITE

GRAPTO-LITE

Calibrating the Time Scale

The geological time scale gives the relative ages of geological events. It indicates that the vast swampy forests, from which the world's great coal deposits are derived, flourished after the Old Red Sandstone of the Devonian Period had been laid down and prior to earth movements which resulted in the uplift of the Appalachians of North America, a range of mountains which probably rivalled the present Alps in height. But it does not indicate the *absolute* age of the Coal Measures, nor the Old Red Sandstone.

It was only the discovery of radioactivity in the closing years of the last century that paved the way for calibrating the geological time scale fairly accurately and thus converting geological or relative time into absolute time. Certain rocks can be dated by the radioactive minerals they contain. For radioactive elements, such as uranium and thorium, gradually break down or *decay* into more stable elements (in these cases lead). Since the rate at which this happens can be calculated, it is possible, by noting the amount of lead produced at the expense of uranium or thorium in such rocks, to determine their age. In practice this is more difficult than it seems, for one gram of uranium will yield just 0·000136 gram of lead in one *million* years. So, a very small error in assessing the uranium/lead ratio means an error of many millions of years in the final calculation of the age of the rock.

Nor is this the only problem, for, generally speaking, radioactive minerals are found in igneous rocks and it is often difficult to date these *geologically*. If the particular igneous rocks happen to occur as a lava flow in sedimentary rock layers then they can easily be dated geologically by the strata immediately above and beneath them. But say they have resulted from the injection of molten material into the sedimentary rocks from below; certainly they are younger than the invaded sedimentary rocks, but how much younger? When the dated igneous rocks can be related closely in age to the associated sedimentary rocks they act as markers in the geological time scale.

heat. A lava flow will only alter the rocks below but an intrusive sill will bake the overlying rocks too.

It is this sort of evidence, patiently collected by geologists, that has gone into the making of geological maps and the geological time scale. When all the details are fitted together it is possible to give a fairly accurate history of an area.

A SUMMARY OF THE EARTH'S HISTORY

DUST AND GASES BEGIN TO CONDENSE...

...AND BY ACCUMULATION THE EARTH IS FORMED BUT THE PLANET IS STILL COLD

THEN RADIOACTIVE DECAY BEGINS TO HEAT UP THE EARTH...

UNTIL IT IS A SEMI-MOLTEN BODY

One theory of the Earth's origin is that it gradually condensed from a mass of dust and gases and later passed through a semi-molten phase.

GRANITE – AN IGNEOUS ROCK
COOLED FROM
A MOLTEN STATE

COARSE SANDSTONE – MADE UP
OF FRAGMENTS OF ERODED ROCK
A SEDIMENTARY ROCK

ONE theory of the Earth's origin is that it gradually condensed from a mass of dust and gases. At first it was probably very cold. Then, as the Sun warmed up and radioactive decay in the Earth set in, the temperature rose, until the Earth became semi-molten.

Only if the Earth was at some time in a molten or semi-molten state could the present distribution of the rocks have been obtained with the lightest rocks at the surface and the denser rocks beneath. When the Earth was first formed the surface was probably very rugged and the ocean basins large hollows. At that time, most of the water must have been in the form of steam up above the surface. The first-formed rocks developed from the semi-molten state and must have been similar to the igneous rocks of the present which crystallize from a molten state. Then, as the Earth cooled, the clouds of steam condensed and rain began to fall. The water attacked the rocks chemically and physically and began to carry sediment down in rivers. These reached the seas and deposited the sands and gravels which were the first sedimentary rocks. But the original surface of the Earth has long since disappeared. No vestige of a beginning has been found. Mountains have been built and destroyed many times during the Earth's history.

19

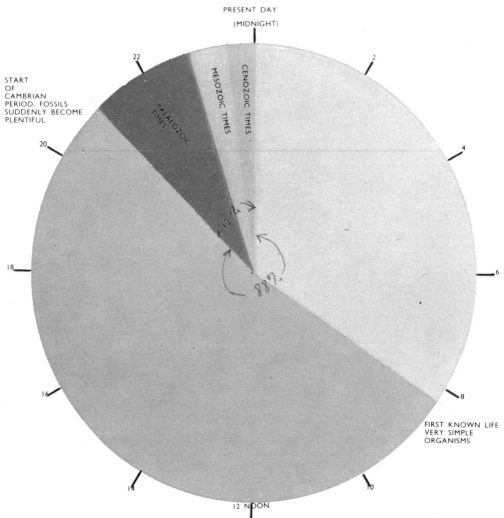

PRESENT DAY
(MIDNIGHT)

START
OF
CAMBRIAN
PERIOD. FOSSILS
SUDDENLY BECOME
PLENTIFUL

PALAEOZOIC
TIMES

MESOZOIC TIMES

CENOZOIC TIMES

FIRST KNOWN LIFE
VERY SIMPLE
ORGANISMS

12 NOON

If the whole of the Earth's history (4,500,000,000 years) were condensed into twenty-four hours, the Cambrian period, which began about 570 million years ago, would begin about nine o'clock in the evening. No life at all would appear until after eight in the morning and then only simple organisms. On this scale Man comes into existence about a quarter of a minute to midnight.

CHAPTER FOUR

The Work of the Geologist

THERE are many stories to unravel from a single piece of rock. It may be that the rock has cooled from a hot molten mass (*igneous* rock). In this case, the type of crystals in the rock will reveal something of the original composition and temperature of the molten mass while the size and form of the crystals will indicate just how fast it cooled.

On the other hand the rock may be *sedimentary* – that is, built up of material weathered from other, older rocks. It may then be possible to find out where the fragments came from by matching them with outcrops of parent rock elsewhere. From the shape of the fragments the agency which displaced them may be revealed – whether wind, water or ice.

To the geologist, whose chief aim is to build up a picture of the Earth's history, all such clues are invaluable. Further clues may be present. The remains of organic life (*fossils*) preserved in sediments may not only enable him to date the rock but possibly, by comparison with forms of life today, may provide evidence of the climate and conditions of the time when the rock was formed. There may be structures in the rocks – mud cracks, ripple marks, or folded and broken layers, all of which have something to reveal of events that have long since passed.

But glimpses of ancient landscapes, seas, and life so faithfully recorded in the Earth's crust are of little value unless they can be put in the order in which they took place – the correct *chronological order*. To do this – to get his chapters in the right sequence – the geologist constructs his map.

The Geological Map

Though the geological map may record in a few square feet millions of years of geological time, there is nothing strange or mysterious about it, or about its construction. The geologist with a hammer, compass and a simple instrument called a *clinometer* goes out into the country and simply marks down on an ordinary (topographical) map those rocks that reach the surface in the particular area he is surveying. In different colours, he shades in the various limestones, sandstones, shales or volcanic lavas just where they occur.

Because of the covering of soil this may often appear difficult. But the geologist soon learns the tricks of his trade. In quarries, cuttings, stream beds and along river banks the underlying rocks can often be found to break the surface. Elsewhere, a gentle change of slope may mark a change in the rock underneath or inspection of fragments thrown up by burrowing rabbits, moles and badgers may be useful. A series of springs, a difference in drainage, even a change of vegetation may be significant enough for the geologist to separate different types of rock.

An outcrop of a rock at the Earth's surface is of course only a section of a layer which is for the most part concealed. One layer rests on top of another, and, according to a principle discovered by the English geologist, William Smith; the upper layer will be

The appearance of a landscape often gives an indication of geological structure. Here a geologist makes use of a high vantage point to sketch in features. Hard rocks form ridges; soft rocks weather into vales. Right, two simple instruments: a compass and a clinometer.

A SIMPLE HOME-MADE CLINOMETER FOR MEASURING THE DIP OF ROCK LAYERS

COMPASS – USED FOR FINDING THE DIRECTION IN WHICH A ROCK LAYER DIPS. THE STRIKE OF THE ROCK – THE DIRECTION WHICH THE ROCK OUTCROP FOLLOWS ACROSS COUNTRY – IS ALSO RECORDED

younger than the lower layer. This is common sense, for the upper layer can only have been deposited at a later time.

Using Smith's so-called Law of *Superposition*, the geologist can find out the relative ages of the rocks in the area he has mapped. He then can relate his map to maps made elsewhere and slowly a fuller picture of the sequence of the rocks is built up.

Cretaceous rocks can be shown to rest on top of older Jurassic rocks while Jurassic rocks themselves lie upon even older Triassic rocks. In some areas the record of rocks deposited in time may be incomplete. Great thicknesses of rock may have been eroded away or alternatively no sediment may have been laid down. Somewhere, however, there are rocks that bridge the gap. Then, with a correct sequence of rock

New techniques provide additional evidence for the geologist. Aerial photographs may give a broad picture of the geology of an area hundreds of miles square. Seismic and magnetic surveys may reveal what rocks and structures lie beneath the surface. Cores from drillings provide direct information about underground rocks.

known, all the individual clues given by the fossils and minerals and structures can be fitted into place. Pictures of each episode of the Earth's history can be built up and also how one episode changed into another.

Structure and the Geological Map

When the layers of rock were formed they were laid down (as they are today) in a more or less horizontal position. If no Earth movements had taken place the horizontal position would be preserved. But throughout geological time, great upheavals have taken place and the layers of rock have been bent, fractured, and tilted.

In his inspection of the rock layers, the geologist discovers not only the relative age of each layer, but also he can learn something of the forces in the crust. This is where his clinometer comes in use. A clinometer is a scale of degrees equipped with a plumbline,

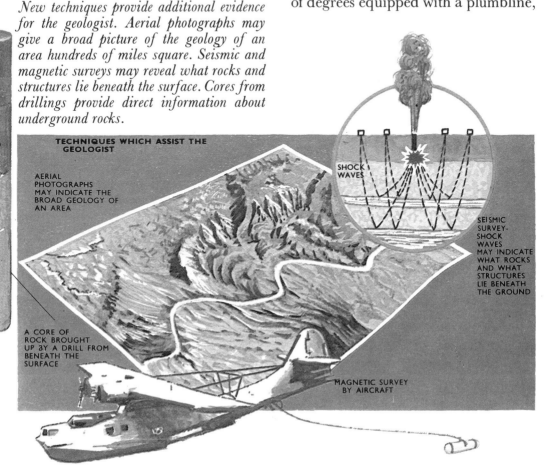

TECHNIQUES WHICH ASSIST THE GEOLOGIST

AERIAL PHOTOGRAPHS MAY INDICATE THE BROAD GEOLOGY OF AN AREA

SHOCK WAVES

SEISMIC SURVEY-SHOCK WAVES MAY INDICATE WHAT ROCKS AND WHAT STRUCTURES LIE BENEATH THE GROUND

A CORE OF ROCK BROUGHT UP BY A DRILL FROM BENEATH THE SURFACE

MAGNETIC SURVEY BY AIRCRAFT

which can be used for measuring the slope or *dip* of the rock layers. The steepness of the dip usually reveals the intensity of the past Earth movements. Once horizontal layers of sediments are perhaps now tilted into an upright position revealing the former presence of great compression forces. Again, a layer of rock may be found to dip under the Earth at one point, only to be discovered breaking the surface a short distance away, dipping in the opposite direction. Here the geologist has discovered a bend or fold in the rocks. The layer does not continue to plunge downwards but has been bent upwards by great forces.

Another problem may be faults in the rock – cracks along which slabs of rock have moved. Faults are also evidence of earth movements and may reveal themselves to the geologist as fault scarps at the surface, or by offsetting outcrops of rock, or simply by repeating outcrops of rock.

By taking into account the tilt of the strata and the folds and faults, the geologist builds up a history of the *structural geology* of the area covered by his map. This will include an estima-

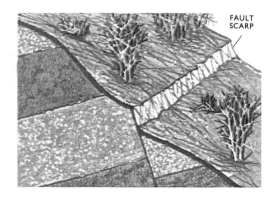

Faults are important for understanding the structure of an area. They may also be important in connection with the occurrence of oil and metal ores. Faults are sometimes

tion of the size and directions of the various forces which have been active.

Application of Geology

The story of the Earth as revealed by the rocks is a fascinating one. But the information built up over the years is not only of historic interest. The Earth provides man with coal, oil, metal ores, even water itself, while the rocks and their structure may be important in siting new buildings, dams and land development schemes. Maps may then not only be important for casting light

The occurrence of rock layers at the surface together with their dip, reveals the geological structure of an area. The illustration shows an anticline as mapped in plan and as reconstructed in section.

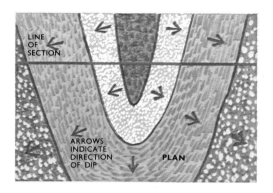

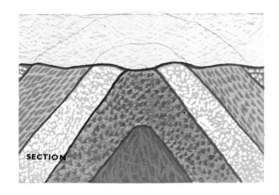

POSITIONS OF FAULTS ARE OFTEN INDICATED BY VALLEYS

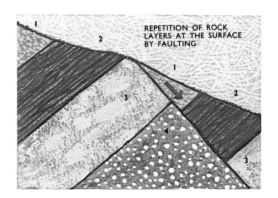

REPETITION OF ROCK LAYERS AT THE SURFACE BY FAULTING

revealed in a landscape as in the two left-hand pictures. Elsewhere their presence may be detected by the repetition *or* cutting-out *of known rock layers.*

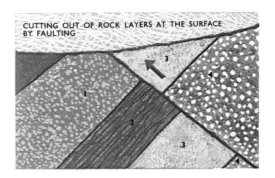

CUTTING OUT OF ROCK LAYERS AT THE SURFACE BY FAULTING

on remote pasts, but in more practical applications which directly benefit man. From knowledge of rock structures, the depth of particularly valuable layers of sediment beneath the surface can be estimated. Perhaps the layer is a coal seam or a mineral vein. It may be water-bearing rock and the geologist can advise where to drill a well.

In searching for oil the best oil fields are associated with certain rock structures which trap the oil. Examples are arched up layers of rock (*anticlines*), salt domes, and faults. By careful mapping the geologist can discover the most likely places for oil to exist. This is valuable information, for the cost of drilling is very great. Bore holes are only sunk in those areas where there is some possibility of success. Otherwise too much money would be spent.

The palaeontologist – a geologist particularly interested in remains of life – can not only date the rocks by the fossils but often he can correlate one bed with another known to be associated with a valuable mineral. There is then a strong possibility of

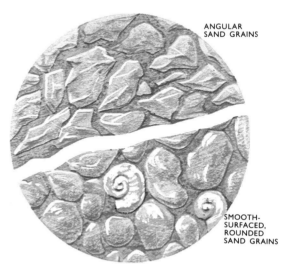

ANGULAR SAND GRAINS

SMOOTH-SURFACED, ROUNDED SAND GRAINS

Top: Sharp-edged, angular sand grains indicate transport by ice. Below: Smoothed, rounded sand grains of regular size suggest that the sediment has been sorted and re-deposited by water.

Geology attempts to reconstruct the entire history of the Earth and its inhabitants. So vast is the subject that for convenience, it is divided into a number of branches. *Physical Geology* is the study of mechanisms in the Earth – causes of uplift and subsidence, processes of weathering and deposition. *Palaeontology* is the study of fossils – the preserved remains of past animals and plants. *Petrology* considers the origin and composition of rocks, while *Mineralogy* deals with the study of the individual minerals making the rocks.

All other branches of science contribute to geology. Physics is particularly useful to physical geology – for instance in understanding Earth movements. Chemistry contributes to mineralogy and petrology while palaeontology is really the 'biology' of the past.

Though a geologist may have a broad knowledge of the whole of his subject, often he will specialize in some particular branch of it.

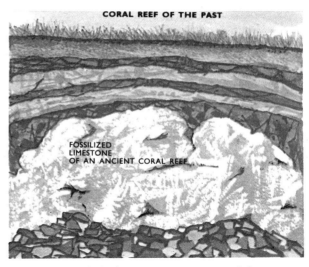

CORAL REEF OF THE PAST

FOSSILIZED LIMESTONE OF AN ANCIENT CORAL REEF

Conditions of the past are reconstructed by comparing structures and fossils preserved in rocks, with similar present-day occurrences.

MODERN CORAL REEF

further mineral discoveries.

New techniques are now used to help the geologist. Samples from experimental bore holes give additional information about underground structure. And so do the geophysical methods of survey which measure the effect of shock waves in the Earth (*seismic* survey), the difference in gravitational attraction (*gravimetric* survey), and the intensity and direction of magnetic fields (*magnetic* survey).

The Skin of
the Earth

CHAPTER FIVE

Sedimentary Rocks

WHATEVER the origin of our planet, it is certain that the earliest rocks solidified in huge masses from a molten or semi-molten state. They must have resembled the granites and basalts that we associate with volcanic activity. These are *igneous* rocks – a term derived from the latin 'ignis' meaning fire. When the Earth cooled and the steam and water vapour of the atmosphere condensed, weathering and erosion of the rocks began. The water and its dissolved gases attacked the rocks and weakened them: streams carried away the loosened material and deposited it elsewhere. These deposits were the first *sedimentary* rocks. Since this time, the rocks have been uplifted and worn down time and time again. The constituent minerals became part of a new sedimentary rock each time but originally this material all came from the igneous rocks.

The term 'sediment' strictly applies to material that settles out from a liquid but the sedimentary rocks include more than this. They include rocks formed from particles that settle on land (e.g. wind-blown sand) as well as in the water. These are *fragmental* rocks, made up of particles from older sediments or igneous rocks. Sedimentary deposits also include *chemical* deposits, for example, rock salt and some limestones that are deposited from solution. The third type of sedimentary rock is the *organic* deposit. Examples include coal, peat and some limestones, all of which are made up of the remains of plants and/or animals. All have in common the fact that they settled layer upon layer. Where the types of sediment varied fairly rapidly (in geological terms) the layers are clearly visible in exposed rocks. The *bedding planes*, parallel to the original surface, are often weak points in sedimentary rocks and it is often possible to split the rocks along these planes. Sediments frequently trap living and dead organisms which may then be preserved as *fossils*. Igneous rocks contain no fossils, except occasional lava flows that sweep up plants and animals.

Fragmental Rocks

These are deposits containing actual particles derived from older rocks by weathering and erosion. They are also called *clastic* deposits. When mechanical weathering is dominant (for example, frost and heat-shattering, glacial or marine erosion), the deposits – scree, boulder-clay and beach gravel

A sample of conglomerate showing the rounded pebbles embedded in a fine-grained matrix.

– contain irregular lumps of rock with a composition very similar to the parent rock. The size of the particles varies enormously – from huge boulders to the finely ground rock-flour of boulder-clay. These rather irregular deposits are called *rudaceous* deposits. When fresh, they resemble the composition of the parent rock but subsequent transport or chemical erosion may alter them considerably. For example a mass of chalk and flint at the base of the chalk cliffs will quickly be reduced to a mass of flint pebbles. The soft chalk is eroded away and the flint nodules are rounded. River gravels, beach deposits and others may later be cemented by silica, lime, etc. contained in per-colating water. They form *conglomerates* if the pebbles are rounded or *breccias* if the stones are angular. Later erosion may remove the cement and leave a secondary rudaceous deposit.

Chemical weathering involves the action of water and its dissolved gases on the rock. Some of the minerals in the rock are more readily attacked than others. Crystals of the more resistant ones are released and form sandy or *arenaceous* deposits. Granite consists mainly of quartz (silica), felspar and mica. The felspar weathers and the other minerals are released. Prolonged transport removes many of the softer and less stable minerals, so that the sands deposited in the lower reaches of rivers, and around the coasts, consist mainly of quartz and mica. In regions of very fine-grained resistant rocks (e.g. basalts) the sand may be made up of particles of the parent rock. Desert sands contain more rounded grains than water-borne sands. The composition depends upon the original rock, for there is little chemical weathering. Quartz again predominates because the softer

Simplified diagram to show the way in which clay or shale becomes altered by pressure into slate. When clay is laid down, the flaky crystals lie parallel to the surface. Immense pressures caused by earth-movements may cause recrystallisation of the minerals in another plane perpendicular to the pressure. The rock, now called slate, can be split in this new plane but not along the original one.

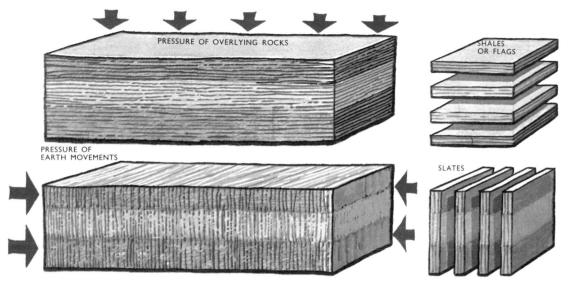

minerals are ground up and blown away by the wind. Water-borne and wind-blown sands are well sorted according to size. The finer particles are carried further and any region of a deposit contains grains of a particular size. Sands carried along by glaciers and deposited by their out-flow streams are completely ·unsorted and very fresh. They are angular and unweathered. Loose sandy deposits may become cemented into sandstones by silica, iron compounds or calcium carbonate from percolating water. In the latter case they form *calcareous sandstones*.

The finest-grained of the fragmental rocks are termed *argillaceous*. Some (a few boulder clays and windblown dust – loess) consist of finely powdered rock and are not fundamentally different from the sandy rocks but the true clays are very different. When felspars and various other minerals decompose on weathering they produce a number of very stable minerals of a flaky nature. These are the *clay minerals* – compounds of aluminium and silica, but their chemistry is still not completely known. These minerals are characteristic of the true clays, but as a rule are mixed with some rock-flour and silt. Clays are carried further in the water and are deposited further out to sea than sands and silts. The large surface area of the flaky minerals adsorbs large amounts of water and this is responsible for the plastic nature of clay. If the overlying sediments become sufficiently heavy, the water is forced out and the minerals recrystallize to form *mudstones* and *shales*. *Slates* are clays that have been altered (*metamorphosed*) by enormous pressures. The flaky minerals have recrystallized so that they lie at right angles to the

direction of pressure and they easily split along these planes.

Chemical Deposits

These are deposits formed by precipitation or crystallization from solution. Many of them are associated with desert deposits. There are, for example, large deposits of rock-salt and gypsum (calcium sulphate) in the Triassic rocks of Britain. Arid climates result in evaporation of water from land-locked seas and lakes and the precipitation of the salts. Chlorides and sulphates are the most important of the chemical deposits but, in certain regions, nitrates, borates and iron deposits are valuable. Some limestones were deposited from solution – e.g., the Oolitic limestone of the Jurassic which is composed of tiny spherical lumps of calcium carbonate. Water running from limestone rocks may coat objects with calcium carbonate. Stalactites and stalagmites

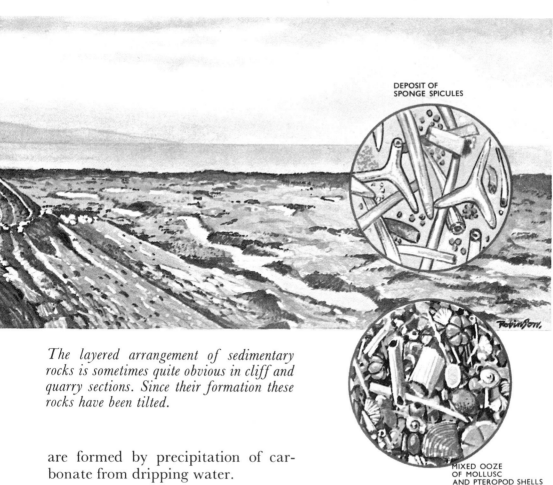

DEPOSIT OF
SPONGE SPICULES

The layered arrangement of sedimentary rocks is sometimes quite obvious in cliff and quarry sections. Since their formation these rocks have been tilted.

MIXED OOZE
OF MOLLUSC
AND PTEROPOD SHELLS

are formed by precipitation of carbonate from dripping water.

Organic Deposits

Coal and oil are the altered remains of animals and plants that accumulated long ago in swamps or on the seabed. These are truly organic sediments. Many limestones are built up of the remains of animals. *Crinoidal* limestone is made up of the skeletons of sea-lilies (*crinoids*). Chalk consists of the skeletons of millions of tiny planktonic animals. The floors of the present-day oceans are covered by various *oozes*, made up of skeletons of radiolarians, foraminiferans, diatoms (tiny plants) and other organisms. These will eventually be consolidated by great pressure or by cementation, and form

GLOBIGERINA
OOZE

Various oozes that are now being formed on the ocean floors from the skeletons of marine organisms.

rocks. Pure organic deposits can build up only far out to sea or around low-lying coasts where there is little other sediment.

CHAPTER SIX

Limestone

THE hard Portland stone used in the building of St. Paul's Cathedral and many other famous buildings, the White Cliffs of Dover, coral reefs and much of the Alps are made up of *Calcareous* rocks (i.e. they consist mainly of calcium carbonate). They are all varieties of *limestone* and fizz strongly when tested with dilute acid. Limestones occur in all geological systems notably the Carboniferous and (in Europe) the Jurassic.

Calcium carbonate occurs in two forms. *Calcite* is the stable crystalline form and is the main mineral of limestones. It is found in the skeletons of many types of invertebrate. *Aragonite*, too, is formed by many animals and it is the form taken by calcium carbonate when it crystallises from solution. Aragonite, however, is unstable in water and is gradually converted to calcite. Limestone rocks therefore contain little or no aragonite although it may have been present in large quantities in the original deposit. Magnesium carbonate is usually present in limestones. When present in fair amounts in the original deposit, the double compound calcium magnesium carbonate may be formed when the rock hardens. The rock is then called *dolomite*.

Present day seas are rarely saturated with calcium carbonate and precipitation of aragonite is not common. However, the Bahamas Bank, between the Bahama Islands and Cuba, has an extensive deposit of aragonite mud. The shallow water does not mix freely with the open sea. High temperatures evaporate much water and concentrate the salts. Aragonite crystals are then deposited. Fine grained calcite rocks such as those of the Carboniferous in south Wales are believed to have been formed as aragonite muds and to have since recrystallised. This area must have had warm, shallow seas too.

Portland stone and some other lime-

Organic limestones are the most common of the calcareous deposits. Some of them consist mainly of the remains of only one type of organism. A good example is *crinoidal limestone*, made up of the remains of sea-lilies (*crinoids*). Most of the limestones are mixed however, being made up of shell fragments and some complete shells. Brachiopods, molluscs, bryozoans, corals, echinoderms, protozoans and crustaceans all add to the deposits. Most of them provide calcite or aragonite but molluscs contribute both. The aragonite shells or parts of the shells may be replaced by calcite or they may disappear altogether, the carbonate recrystallising as calcite cement around the other fragments. Reef limestones are formed of the skeletons of corals together with lime-secreting algae and other organisms. The material is cemented as it is formed by the organisms.

Chalk is an extremely pure form of limestone especially characteristic of the upper Cretaceous period. It is almost entirely calcite and is not normally cemented – it can be crumbled quite easily. Chalk is made up of the remains of various planktonic organisms together with shells and shell fragments and frequently contains flints. It appears to be a shallow-water deposit, not related to *globigerina ooze*, a calcareous deposit now accumulating on much of the ocean floor.

stones are made up of millions of tiny spheres cemented tightly together. These rocks resemble masses of fish eggs and are called *oolites*. The individual grains are perhaps one millimetre across and are made up of numerous concentric layers of calcite surrounding a nucleus which may be a quartz grain or a shell fragment. Modern oolites are being formed in the Red Sea and around the Bahamas. Aragonite is being deposited and where the currents or wave action roll the grains around, they become

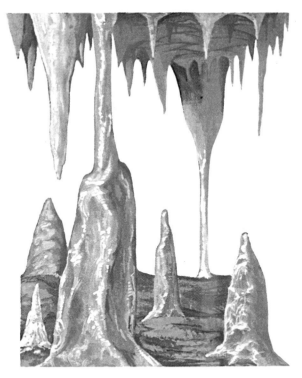

Stalactites (*top*) *and* stalagmites *develop wherever water drips out from limestone rocks. Impurities such as iron or manganese may stain the rocks striking colours.*

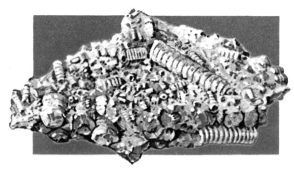

The sea-lilies, as shown below, played an important part of life in some ancient seas. Some limestones (above) consist almost entirely of their cylindrical stems and arms.

spherical and continue to gather more carbonate. These modern deposits will presumably become altered to calcite in time. Rocks with larger grains than the oolites are called *pisolites*.

Although limestones may be very hard they are easily attacked by water. The dissolved carbon dioxide forms a weak acid, which dissolves some of the rock. *Limestone pavements* are formed because water enlarges the joints into deep furrows. Water running through limestones dissolves out caverns and becomes charged with calcium bicarbonate. Upon evaporation of the water the carbonate reforms and may be deposited as *tufa* or as *stalactites* and *stalagmites* if the water drops from a cave roof.

CHAPTER SEVEN

Igneous and Metamorphic Rocks

THE crust of the Earth is believed to have solidified from molten rock or *magma*. Today it forms a skin surrounding a hotter interior zone where rock can still exist in this molten condition.

Despite the apparent firmness and solidity, the crust is subjected to enormous strains and stresses. At some

surface are termed *extrusive*. The magma from which they are formed may vary in composition and properties. Thick and treacly magma will form massive steep-sided mountains – the familiar cones of many of our volcanoes. Pockets of trapped gas eventually escape causing violent explosions. Fragments of half-cooled

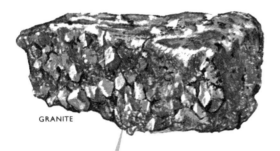

GRANITE

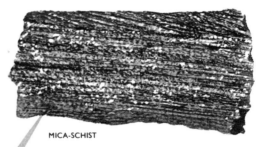

MICA-SCHIST

Left. Granite, an example of a slowly-cooled igneous rock. Right. Mica-schist – a metamorphic rock in which platey recrystallized micas have been arranged with their surfaces at right-angles to the pressure. Below. Sections of these rocks under the microscope. Note the well-developed crystals in the granite.

points, weaknesses in the surface may develop through which magma can surge. Examples of these are our present-day volcanoes. Volcanic action with the spectacular eruption of glowing lava has given rise to the term *igneous* (Latin, ignis = a fire) used in describing rocks thought to have formed from a molten state.

The igneous rocks cooled on the

rock are then thrown into the air. Sometimes the lumps are quite large – 9 inches to a foot in length. These are the *volcanic bombs*. As they descend, they twist and turn and the soft rock becomes spindle-shaped. Smaller particles are called lapilli meaning 'little stones', while the finest dust forms a volcanic ash. The molten rock itself flows as a lava and solidifies, giving off gases. Small cavities or vesicles may, as a result, be formed inside the rock giving a 'frothy' appearance. *Pumice stone* is a well known example of this phenomenon.

If the magma is more fluid, instead of forming steep volcanoes, it will flow in thin sheets over very large

The Classification of Igneous Rocks

The elements silicon and oxygen readily combine to form silicon dioxide or *silica* (SiO_2). This is a very important mineral. In a molten state it behaves as an acid, combining with any metallic oxides present, to form a very common and important group of minerals – the *silicates*.

The quantity of silica present in the original magma is used in classifying the resulting igneous rock. If a lot of silica is present, it will combine with all the metal oxides present, and some free silica will remain. Rocks of this nature are said to be *acidic*. If only a small quantity of silica remains in the uncombined state, the rocks are described as *intermediate*. The so-called *basic* rocks have even less silica and none of it remains in the free state. Finally, there are sometimes found heavy, dark, *ultra-basic* rocks, so poor in silica that none of the metal oxides is completely converted to silicates.

All four types of rock may cool either slowly, deep in the crust (*plutonic*), rapidly on the Earth's surface (*volcanic*) or at an intermediate speeds near the surface (*hypabyssal*). In the table a working classification of the igneous rocks is shown.

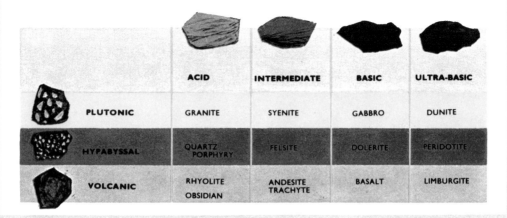

	ACID	INTERMEDIATE	BASIC	ULTRA-BASIC
PLUTONIC	GRANITE	SYENITE	GABBRO	DUNITE
HYPABYSSAL	QUARTZ PORPHYRY	FELSITE	DOLERITE	PERIDOTITE
VOLCANIC	RHYOLITE OBSIDIAN	ANDESITE TRACHYTE	BASALT	LIMBURGITE

areas. The islands of Hawaii are made up of such sheets of basalt, a dark, easily-flowing lava. Most of this enormous expanse lies beneath the sea. As a rule all extrusive rocks are predominantly glassy in structure since they cool too rapidly for crystals to form.

Some magma never reaches the surface but cools within the earth. The igneous rocks formed are then termed *intrusive*. If the magma was injected into sedimentary layers along bedding planes, the igneous sheet formed is called a *sill* and is said to be *conformable* with the surrounding rock. Sometimes, the magma forces its way across strata at angles to the bedding planes.

These structures are called *dykes* and they are said to be *unconformable*. It may happen that the magma is forced through a comparatively small aperture in the layers and reaches an area where it is actually able to lift up the layers of overhead rock. A bun-shaped intrusion or *laccolith* is then formed. Alternatively the magma may cause strata beneath it to sag, in which case a basin-shaped intrusion or *lopolith* develops. Laccoliths and lopoliths are often very rich in valuable minerals. A large lopolith at Sudbury, Ontario, produces nearly three-quarters of the world's nickel.

Dykes, sills and lava flows come from huge chambers of magma that may be several miles below the surface. Usually the magma cools at an intermediate rate producing an intermediate structure, either a glassy base containing a few large crystals or a ground mass of very fine crystals. Such rock is described as *hypabyssal*. In some areas, such as Cornwall or Scotland, the igneous activity finished many millions of years ago. Here, even the magma chambers themselves have solidified. Rocks cooled at such great depths below the Earth's surface are termed *plutonic* after the Roman god of the underworld, Pluto. The time taken for solidification to be completed may be a million years. Crystals large enough to be seen with the naked eye are able to form. Examples of such crystalline rocks are *granite*, usually light-coloured (pink or grey), and the dark, heavy *gabbros*.

Erosion may lay bare these old magma reservoirs. When of great size they are called *batholiths*. Sometimes the roof of a batholith extends upwards into many domes and it is thought that the granite masses of Cornwall and the Scilly Isles are six domes of the same underlying batholith. One of the largest batholiths, in the United States, is over 1,000 miles long and 150 miles wide.

Metamorphic Rocks

Both igneous and sedimentary rocks may be altered by pressures or high temperature into completely different

Magma from a single chamber may reach the Earth's surface as volcanic larva or it may cool inside the crust in a variety of different shaped intrusions. Over a very long period the magma in the chamber may itself cool into rock.

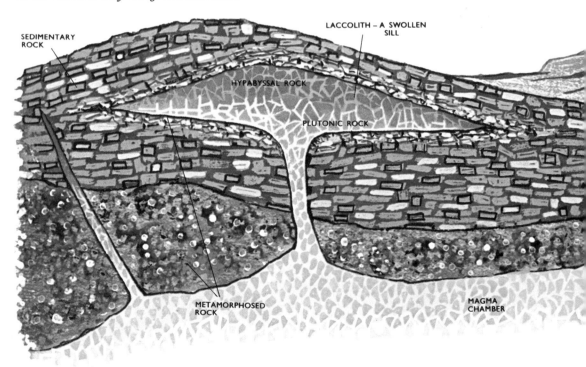

SEDIMENTARY ROCK

LACCOLITH – A SWOLLEN SILL

HYPABYSSAL ROCK

PLUTONIC ROCK

METAMORPHOSED ROCK

MAGMA CHAMBER

forms. The process is one of metamorphism and the new rocks are termed *metamorphic*.

Heat from upsurging magma may alter the crystalline form or even the mineral constitution of the surrounding rocks. This process is described as *thermal metamorphism*. Shales, for instance, may be altered into hornfels, granites to layered gneiss and limestones recrystallized into marbles.

Metamorphism of surrounding rock may often be used to tell whether an igneous layer is a sill or lava flow which has become covered with later sediments. In the case of the sill, thermal metamorphism will have taken place on either side of the

intrusion; a lava flow will metamorphose only the rocks beneath since its upper surface is in contact with the open air. About large intrusions, a surrounding zone (or aureole) of thermally metamorphosed rock may be several miles thick.

Though pressure alone can bring about a few mineral transformations, its more noticeable effect is in causing new slatey or needle-like minerals to crystallize with their flat faces or long axes at right angles to the pressure. In this way, roofing slates are formed from shales. The so-called *slatey cleavage* possessed by slates is thus in no way connected with the original bedding planes of the sediments. Change caused by pressure is termed *dynamic* metamorphism. Often, heat and pressure combine on a large scale causing alterations in rocks over great areas. This is *regional* metamorphism, and is an important feature of mountain building.

For a long time it was a mystery as to what had happened to the country rock in regions where batholiths had formed. Huge batholiths, hundreds of square miles in surface area, are not uncommon Where is the original rock? One theory is that the surrounding rock, or rather the material of which it was composed, is still present in the batholiths. Under the influence of increased temperature, possibly caused by the seeping in of hot rock 'juices' from even further beneath, the country rock itself developed into a magma. This process is termed *ultra-metamorphism*. Thus a cycle is complete. Igneous rocks form from a magma. They are eroded and give rise to sedimentary rocks. These under intense temperatures, may be reconverted to magma from which more igneous rock can develop.

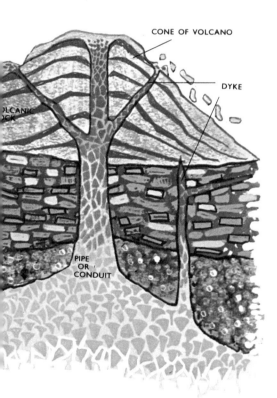

CONE OF VOLCANO

DYKE

VOLCANIC ROCK

PIPE OR CONDUIT

CHAPTER EIGHT

Folds and Faults

COLOSSAL forces have been active in the Earth's crust at many stages during geological time. Though such forces may have long since disappeared, evidence of their earlier activity is left behind in the bent, twisted and fractured rocks at the surface of the Earth. Bends in the rock – rather like wrinkles in a crooked table-cloth – are called *folds*; fractures in the crust along which slabs of rock have moved are called *faults*.

Episodes of faulting and folding are very useful for dividing up geological time into smaller, more convenient units. Rocks older than a given set of Earth movements will be consequently bent and broken; younger (later) rocks will not be affected but will rest on the disturbed surface.

Folding of Rocks

Squeezing, or *compression*, pushes objects tightly together and, unless they are very elastic, forces them to expand in some other direction. When layers of rock are squeezed from the sides, one way of relieving the pressure is for them to expand upwards to form a fold or arch. The same effect can easily be produced by pushing the opposite sides of a paper-backed book together.

An enormous pressure acting over a large area may form a series of such folds in rock, all lying parallel to one another. Each upward fold or arch is called an *anticline* while the troughs in between are called *synclines*. Where the pressure disappears or becomes smaller, the folding gradually dies out and the arch *plunges* into rocks that have not been disturbed.

The size and shape of folds vary according to the directions and intensities of the forces involved and also according to the nature of the rock material.

A tear fault offsetting rocks.

Soft rocks such as clay, gypsum and rock-salt are not brittle. Under pressure they behave something like soft Plasticine. They cannot transmit pressure very far and soon collapse into numerous, irregular, small wrinkles. Rigid rocks such as limestones and sandstones can transmit pressure over a very wide area and large folds, often miles across, may form.

The disturbed surface usually consists of layers of both rigid and soft rocks; while the rigid rocks are bent into large folds, the soft material is squeezed and stretched in between.

Moderate pressures usually form symmetrical folds that stand upright and have each side or *limb* inclined at the same angle. A very strong force acting in the opposite direction to a small force, tends to turn the fold over. Folds representing all stages from upright symmetrical folds to the completely over-turned *recumbent folds* are known.

Two very large forces compressing only slightly rigid rock may completely concertina the folds so that all the limbs are parallel to one another (*isoclinal folds*). Under such compression, more rigid layers of rocks may form folds shaped like fans (*fan folds*). If compression takes place from

The symmetry of folds depends upon the strength, position and direction of the forces responsible.

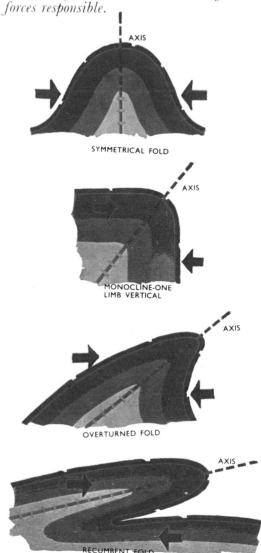

SYMMETRICAL FOLD

MONOCLINE-ONE LIMB VERTICAL

OVERTURNED FOLD

RECUMBENT FOLD

(Left) When rocks can fold no more, faulting may then take place. (Right) Imbricate structure-crustal shortening takes place by slices of rock moving over each other.

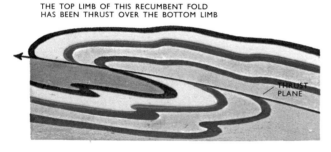

THE TOP LIMB OF THIS RECUMBENT FOLD HAS BEEN THRUST OVER THE BOTTOM LIMB

THRUST PLANE

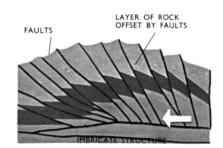

FAULTS

LAYER OF ROCK OFFSET BY FAULTS

IMBRICATE STRUCTURE

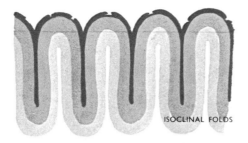

ISOCLINAL FOLDS

The limbs of the intensely squeezed isoclinal folds have become parallel. Fan folds have rigid outside layers and centres of soft rock.

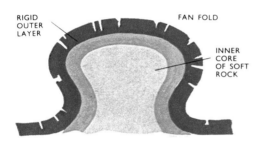

RIGID OUTER LAYER

FAN FOLD

INNER CORE OF SOFT ROCK

Weathering of faulted and folded rocks gives variety to a landscape as depicted in this scene.

Faults, Folds and the Past

Faults and folds are not haphazardly scattered about the Earth's surface in any sort of fashion. Instead they occur in systems – each system representing a particular episode of Earth movement. Most large-scale movements are connected with *orogenies* – the buckling and bending of deep-water troughs in which sediments have accumulated for millions of years.

To the geologist, disturbed rocks are a very useful key to the past. Detailed study of folds and faults shows from which direction the forces involved came. Further, the geography can be reconstructed showing how the disturbed rocks must have been arranged before the distortions took place.

Rocks in some areas show signs of many separate episodes of Earth movement. The first set of folds and faults may be twisted by a second force coming from a different direction.

Usually, the older the rock the more distorted it is; old rocks have been subjected to more Earth movements. However, in particularly stable areas of the crust this is not so. Blue clays covering parts of West Russia are 550 million years old – equivalent to ancient, folded Cambrian rocks of Wales – and yet they are as soft and undisturbed as present-day clays.

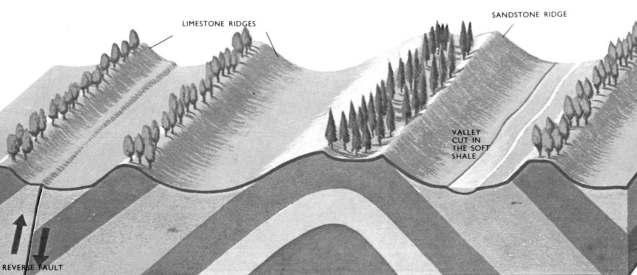

LIMESTONE RIDGES

SANDSTONE RIDGE

VALLEY CUT IN THE SOFT SHALE

REVERSE FAULT

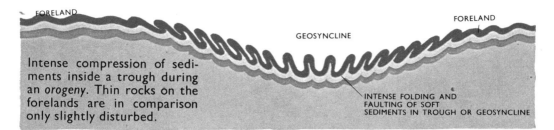

Intense compression of sediments inside a trough during an *orogeny*. Thin rocks on the forelands are in comparison only slightly disturbed.

FORELAND

GEOSYNCLINE

FORELAND

INTENSE FOLDING AND FAULTING OF SOFT SEDIMENTS IN TROUGH OR GEOSYNCLINE

all directions, a circular *dome* will be produced instead of an elongated arch.

Faulting of Rocks

Faults are cracks or fractures in the crust along which rocks can move. Three distinct types of fault are recognized according to the direction in which most movement has taken place. When the Earth's surface is under compression, as well as folding, pressure can be relieved by upward movement of one block of rock over another. Such faults are called *reverse* faults. If the fracture is inclined nearer the horizontal than the vertical, the reverse fault is called a *thrust*. Blocks of rock have been pushed scores of miles from their original positions along thrust planes.

When a section of the Earth's surface is under tension (that is, when forces are stretching the crust) blocks of rock drop downwards along fractures. These are the *normal* faults. States of tension are usually set up after a strong episode of compression in which reverse faulting and folding has taken place.

The third type of faults – the *tear* faults – are distinguished by the mainly horizontal direction of rock movement. For their formation there must be two forces acting in opposite directions but positioned slightly apart. A *couple* or shearing force results which tends to twist the rocks in between. The tear fractures form at approximately 45° to each opposing force and movement along them relieves the stress. Tear faults, such as the Great Glen Fault of Scotland, are very straight and very upright. Rocks are known to have been moved hundreds of miles along tears, though generally the distances are much smaller.

CHAPTER NINE

Soils

SOILS are deposits formed by the physical, chemical and biological action on the underlying rocks or drift material (i.e. boulder-clay or river alluvium). Temperature changes tend to shatter rocks, and rainwater, with its dissolved gases, helps to break up the rocks and release the mineral crystals. Lichens and bacteria are the first organisms to colonise such places. They break up the rock fragments even more and their decayed remains add organic matter to the developing soil. Mosses and higher plants soon follow and add more organic matter to the soil. This organic matter, called *humus*, is the most important single factor in soil.

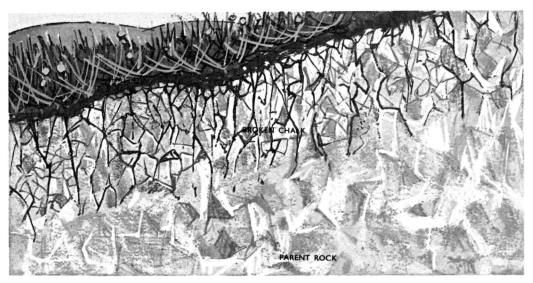

A rendzina *soil typical of chalk downland. The very thin soil lies over the solid rock. Rendzina soils are alkaline or neutral and support a very characteristic collection of plants.*

The Composition of Soil

As soils develop from the underlying rocks it is obvious that they will contain a good deal of *mineral matter*. The size of the particles and their chemical nature depends upon the rock below but in older soils, quartz grains are the commonest minerals. They are the most stable of all minerals and become more and more concentrated as the others are washed away. The size of the mineral particles determines the nature of the soil. There is an international scale concerning the classification of particle sizes.

> Particles more than 2 millimetres in diameter are *gravels* or *stones*.
> Particles 0·2 – 2·0 mm in diameter are *coarse sand*.
> Particles 0·02 – 0·2 mm in diameter are *fine sand*.
> Particles 0·002 – 0·02 mm in diameter are *silt*.
> Particles less than 0·002 mm in diameter are *clay*.

The mineral particles form the 'soil skeleton', holding the other components around or between them.

Soil water is of three types. Drainage water derived from rain and snow runs down through the soil between the particles. It is not always present, of course, and is not important in plant nutrition. Capillary water is held on the surfaces of the particles and the roots in the soils and is not immediately dependent upon rain. As water evaporates from the surface more is drawn up from below to fill the spaces. In a very sandy soil, with large particles and large spaces, water cannot rise by capillary action and the surface layers dry out in hot weather. Capillary water is the main reservoir on which plants draw. Absorbed water (i.e. water actually taken up by the soil particles) is not available to plants. Sandy soils absorb little water but clays, with their tiny particles and huge surface area, absorb a great deal. Humus also absorbs much water.

Humus is decayed and decaying organic matter. It is dark brown or black and rather jelly-like. This last feature gives humus its water-holding capacity. Chemically, humus must be very complicated although it behaves as a single substance. One very important property is its ability to link up with clay particles and form them into tiny groups. Thus humus is a valuable aid to making clay soils workable. It also gives sandy soils the ability to hold water.

Soil atmosphere is essential for the proper growth of plants and other soil organisms, including the useful bacteria. In a waterlogged soil, water takes the place of the air and decomposition is not completed. The soil then becomes acidic and will support only a limited range of plants.

Mineral salts, essential for plant growth, occur in the soil and dissolve in the soil water. Other plant foods are provided by the organic matter. All must dissolve before the plants can use them.

Soil flora and fauna is a term covering all the living organisms of the soil. Perhaps the most important of these are the *bacteria*. These tiny organisms – not quite either plant or animal – act upon the organic material of humus and release soluble salts for use as plant food. Other bacteria 'fix' free nitrogen and convert it to nitrates which can be used by plants. These bacteria are valuable members of the soil community but all require a good supply of oxygen. In waterlogged soils, other bacteria become important and these do not complete the processes of decay.

Apart from bacteria, fungi and protozoan animals are important soil organisms. Earthworms, although not so numerous, have a great deal of influence in the soil. They drag down leaves and aerate the soil with their tunnels. Their droppings, too, affect the soil for they contain a high proportion of calcium carbonate from the 'chalk glands'. Moles, mice and insects all modify the soil in their surroundings and together all these living things make up the world of the soil.

Soil Texture

One has only to talk to gardeners to realise how widely the soil varies. In some places it is almost solid clay, in others, little more than sand. These are two extremes of texture – the

Many experiments can be performed with soil. This one shows how the relative permeability of sandy and clay soils can be demonstrated. Water still sits on the clay surface long after the sand has dried out.

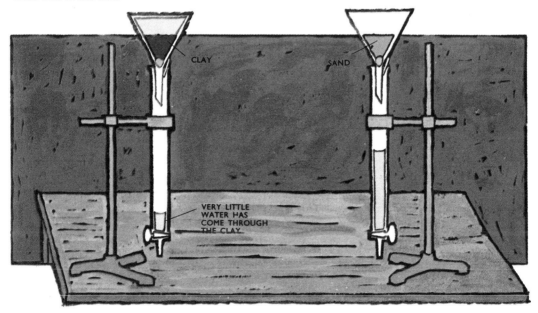

CLAY

SAND

VERY LITTLE
WATER HAS
COME THROUGH
THE CLAY

heavy and the light – and between them lies a range of soils called *loams*. A clay-soil contains a high proportion of tiny particles of clay-mineral. The distance between these particles is minute and the surface tension of the water film holds them tightly together. Clay soils are thus heavy and hard to dig. The small air spaces do not allow good drainage and the soil tends to become waterlogged. Mineral salts are not washed out by rain. During drought, the clay continues to hold a good deal of water and provides a firm hold for roots.

Sandy soils are light soils. Their large mineral particles (mainly grains of quartz) enclose large air-spaces and thus give good aeration of the soil and good drainage. The soils break up easily while digging but mineral foods are quickly lost as they are washed down to the sub-soil.

A good soil contains particles of all sizes so that drainage is neither too fast nor too slow. It also contains plenty of humus to hold water and to provide plant foods. Soils with mixed particle sizes are called *loams*. The particles are not haphazardly arranged but tend to aggregate in small 'crumbs'. This crumb-structure is essential for a good soil – it provides air-spaces and also ensures that the finer particles are not free to be washed down to clog the lower spaces. The soil can easily be worked over. How the particles join up to form 'crumbs' is still a mystery. Each crumb contains all the soil constituents. Sandy soils can be improved by adding humus – it coats the mineral grains and holds water. Clay (heavy) soils are also improved by adding humus. The latter joins with the clay particles and tends to make them join in little groups – producing the crumb structure. Lime has the same effect.

Limestone rocks are usually very pure and as calcium carbonate is soluble in water, limestones do not produce thick soils by themselves. Prolonged solution of the carbonate may result in a thin layer of impurities – silica and clay minerals – forming on the top. These thin soils are called *rendzinas*. They are usually very alkaline but occasionally become acid because all the calcium is leached away by percolating rainwater.

Climate and the Soil

Although the above soil textures depend largely upon the underlying rocks, in the long run, climate has the greatest effect and overrides the action of the parent rocks. Each climatic region favours a certain type of soil formation if left alone. It must be realised of course that a great deal of the land has been cultivated – a process that interferes with the natural process of soil formation. Large areas, too, were affected by the great Ice Age and the soils are still quite young. The climatic soil types are not many and are grouped according to the appearance in section, as in a quarry. This appearance is called the *soil profile*.

In the polar and tundra regions the soils are poorly formed and are termed *skeletal*. They consist mainly of shattered rock fragments for chemical and biological activity is low. Occasional peat soils are formed where mosses and lichens flourish. The cold and cool temperate regions, including much of northern Eurasia and North America, favour a type of soil, called a *podsol*. Rainfall exceeds evaporation and the dominant movement of water is downwards. Humus and minerals (notably iron) are washed down from the surface layers, leaving a bleached zone – the *A horizon*. The materials are deposited lower down in the *B horizon* and form a dark layer. It may become

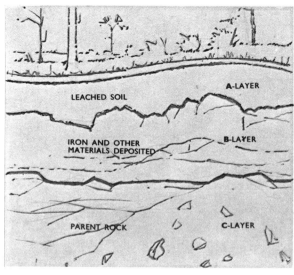

LEACHED SOIL

A-LAYER

IRON AND OTHER
MATERIALS DEPOSITED

B-LAYER

PARENT ROCK

C-LAYER

The profile of a typical podsol formed by leaching of the minerals from the surface. The layers are shown in the diagram.

Earthworms play a large part in conditioning soils. They drag down leaves and provide humus; their worm casts contain calcium carbonate and acid bacterial decay, and their tunnels help to aerate the soil.

solid and form a *hard pan* which prevents further drainage. Waterlogging and peat formation occur in undisturbed land. The warm-temperate regions favour a soil called a *brown forest earth*. Evaporation is nearly equal to rainfall (exceeding it in summer) and leaching is not extensive. Good supplies of humus keep the surface layers brown.

In the semi-arid regions, evaporation exceeds rain-fall and the dominant water movement is upwards, bringing calcium and other salts with it. Humus accumulates in the surface layers which become black. This type of soil is typical of the steppes and prairies and is called *chernosem* or black earth.

Tropical regions are normally wet but rain may be highly seasonal. In this case, the minerals are washed down from the surface and then, in the dry-season, are returned in the capillary water and precipitated at the surface. Iron and aluminium hydroxides are left in an insoluble state and tend to accumulate as a reddish deposit called *laterite*. If aluminium is dominant, the deposit is called *bauxite* – the main ore of aluminium. The soil then becomes infertile because of impeded drainage.

The Restless
Earth

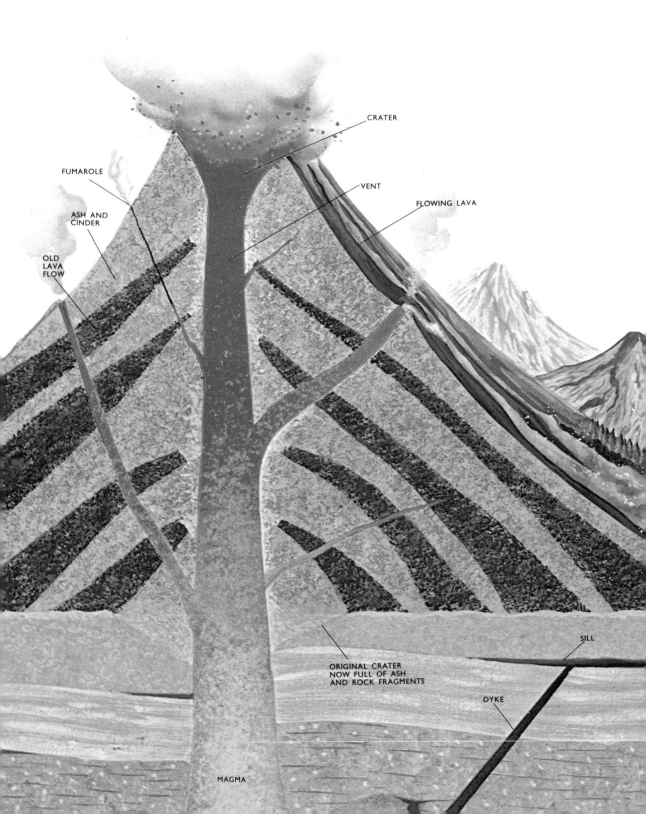

A simplified section through a stratified volcano showing alternating beds of lava and ashes.

CRATER

FUMAROLE

VENT

ASH AND
CINDER

FLOWING LAVA

OLD
LAVA
FLOW

ORIGINAL CRATER
NOW FULL OF ASH
AND ROCK FRAGMENTS

SILL

DYKE

MAGMA

CHAPTER TEN

Volcanic Eruptions

HISTORICAL and geological records show that volcanic activity has been a feature of the Earth's history from the earliest times. The destruction of Pompeii and Herculaneum by Vesuvius in A.D. 79, and the devastation caused by the eruption of Krakatoa in 1883, bear witness to the power of volcanic activity but even these events fade when compared with events of the distant past. To take but one example, there is an area of about one quarter of a million square miles in the North Western United States that is completely covered with volcanic lava.

There are many types of volcanic activity but the term 'volcano' is usually restricted to those cone-shaped mountains which periodically shoot out molten rock (*lava*) and hot ashes. One of the most popular theories of the origin of volcanoes was the 'central fire' theory which held that under the surface layers, the Earth was a seething mass of molten rock. Weak points in the crust allowed the gases to escape and so acted as safety valves. This theory has been discarded, however, because it has been proved that the material thrown out by a volcano originates within about twenty miles of the surface. Investigations with echo-sounding and similar devices have also shown that it is unlikely that there are any extensive masses of molten rock anywhere within about two thousand miles of the Earth's surface. How, then, does the rock become molten and what forces it to the surface?

No really adequate explanation has yet been put forward, but it is significant that almost all the active volcanoes are found in regions that have been recently (geologically speaking) disturbed by mountain-building or other extensive earth-movements – regions such as Italy, Indonesia and Central America. Perhaps frictional forces within the Earth raise the temperature sufficiently to melt the rock and cause it to expand. This molten rock (*magma*) would follow any lines of weakness and may reach the surface. The explosive force of an eruption is

Various types of intrusion of volcanic material into sedimentary rocks.

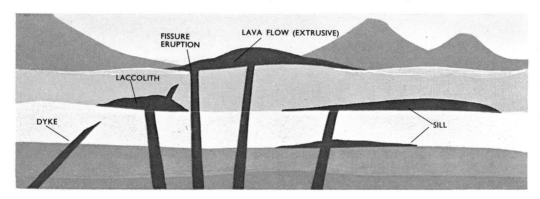

S.R.W.—D

due mainly to the violent expansion of steam and other gases released from the magma as it nears the surface.

When a volcano is first formed (this has been witnessed several times, notably in Mexico in 1943), the exploding gases force their way to the surface and may create a considerable crater as the rock is blown away. Unless the explosion is extremely violent, the broken rocks (*pyroclasts*) and cinders fall around the mouth forming the typical mound (*ash cone*). Later development depends very much on the composition of the magma. If the latter has a low silica content and a high proportion of iron and magnesium compounds, it is mobile and loses its gas easily producing a free flowing *lava* (Magma that has lost its gas). Continuous eruption of this type of lava forms volcanic cones with shallow slopes. Mauna Loa in Hawaii is the classic example. It rises 30,000 feet from the sea floor and, at the base, is about 70 miles across.

Eruption is not normally continuous – only limited amounts of magma are formed at one time. Between eruptions the volcano is said to be '*dormant*'. When eruption ceases the lava solidifies in the centre of the cone (*vent*) and this is what makes dormant volcanoes dangerous. If the magma begins to rise again, enormous pressures will be built up and will eventually overcome the resistance of the solidified lava. The result is a violent explosion, scattering rock fragments, dust and ashes into the air. The same effect occurs when the lava has a high proportion of silica. It is viscous and tends to block the cone and promote spasmodic eruptions. This has happened several times with Vesuvius, forming a *stratified cone*, made up of alternating layers of rocks and ashes, and lava. The devastating Krakatoa explosion in 1883 was similarly caused by a blocked volcanic neck. Much of the island was destroyed and a tidal wave drowned thousands of people in Java and Sumatra.

There are many ancient volcanoes in the world that have not erupted for millions of years. These are called *extinct volcanoes*. The forces of erosion act on them as on all other features of the landscape and wear them down.

Part of the Giants' Causeway on the coast of Northern Ireland. It is part of an old lava flow which, on cooling, developed the typical 6-sided columnar appearance.

It often happens that the solidified magma in the cone (*volcanic plug*) is harder than the surrounding rock and stands out, after a period of erosion, as a *volcanic neck*. Edinburgh Castle is built on such a structure.

Although the *central vent* type of volcano is the most familiar, it is geologically less important than the *fissure eruption*. Here, lava wells up along cracks in the Earth's surface and may cover vast areas of land. The lava flows of North Western U.S.A. have already been mentioned. An even bigger covering of plateau lava must have existed to the North and West of Britain. Remnants of this are found in Greenland, Iceland, Scotland and Ireland but most of it is now under the sea. The Giants' Causeway in Northern Ireland and the lavas of the Isle of Staffa both show the typical six-sided columns into which this sort of lava develops. It is due to contraction on cooling, much as the mud of a dried-up pond forms six-sided plates.

Central and fissure eruptions are examples of *extrusive activity*, but often the magma solidifies before reaching the surface. This is *intrusive volcanic activity*. Dykes, sills and laccoliths are features created by intrusive volcanic activity.

CHAPTER ELEVEN

Earthquakes

THE presence of marine fossils in rocks that are now thousands of feet above sea-level provides sure evidence of movements of the Earth's crust. Such movements are usually extremely slow but they may result in increased tension within the rocks. The tension may be such that the rocks split, forming a *fault*. The vibrations set up by the shearing of the rocks and any movement along the fault plane are transmitted through the Earth as an *earthquake*. Quakes may also occur as a result of movement along an old fault plane. Other causes include volcanic explosions, landslides and cave-falls, but these are usually relatively slight and local in effect.

The majority of earthquakes originate from fault-movements within the upper fifty miles of the crust. The place of origin is called the *focus* and from it the vibrations spread out in all directions. Their speed depends upon the density of the rocks, being greatest in solid granites and least in loose sands and gravels. The intensity of the vibrations falls off as the distance travelled increases. Directly above the focus, on the surface of the ground is the *epicentre*. This is the first point to be affected, and suffers the greatest damage. Away from the epicentre the vibrations are less intense. Lines joining up points of equal intensity are called *isoseismals* and enclose a number of *isoseismic* zones. If the Earth's crust were made up of only one type of rock, these zones would be circular, but local rock variations destroy the regularity.

It is possible to count and measure the vibrations of an earthquake by using instruments, but a simple scale has been devised for estimating intensity. This is the *Mercalli Scale*. At the lower end of the scale are the very feeble quakes that are detected only by

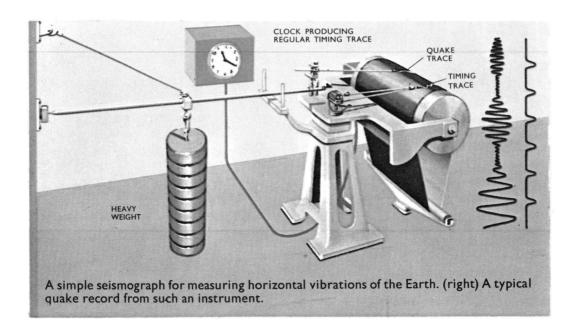

A simple seismograph for measuring horizontal vibrations of the Earth. (right) A typical quake record from such an instrument.

delicate instruments. At the other end is the catastrophic earthquake which produces yawning crevices in the ground and destroys everything. Between these extremes, features such as the ringing of bells and the cracking of walls are used as guides. Earthquake intensity can thus be judged by ordinary people with no training, and their observations are useful in plotting isoseismic zones and determining the epicentre of the quake.

Although quakes can, in theory, occur anywhere, there are two main belts which, between them, account for more than 80% of the disturbances of modern times. The *Circum-Pacific belt*, running from Chile, north to Alaska and then down through Japan to New Guinea is the larger of the two. The *Mediterranean belt* extends from Spain and North Africa, through Italy and the Middle East, to join the Circum-Pacific belt in the East Indies. Minor belts occur along the Mid-Atlantic and in the Rift Valley of East Africa. All these regions are associated with the most recent periods of mountain-building or other major earth movements, and are characterised by steep slopes, often under the sea. Quakes centred under the sea usually produce huge waves that do more damage than the quakes themselves. Minor tremors experienced in Northern Europe are ascribed to the intermittent uplift of the rocks which are still rising after the melting of the Ice Age glaciers.

Seismographs and Seismic Waves

The study of earthquakes is called *seismology* (size-mology) and the instruments used in their detection are called *seismographs*. Recording stations all over the world make continuous records of earth-tremors. Dozens are recorded daily in some regions but most of these indicate minor quakes or stronger ones deep down in the earth.

Seismographs can record either horizontal or vertical vibrations in the earth. In its simplest form the seismograph consists of a heavy weight suspended on an arm from a rigid support. Horizontal vibrations of the Earth are transmitted to the support but the inertia of the weight tends to keep it still. A rotating drum also vibrates with the earth and receives an inked trace or a photographic trace from the end of the weighted arm.

The trace produced by a typical earthquake (assuming it is not powerful enough to damage the instrument) shows three distinct regions. These correspond to the three types of wave set up by a quake. The first waves to reach the observer are the '*push and pull*' waves that travel in the manner of sound waves (i.e. they vibrate in the direction of travel). After these waves come the 'shake' waves that vibrate at right angles to the direction of travel. The '*shake*' waves are the slower of the two and the time that passes between the arrival of the two groups determines the distance of the focus from the observer. The third type of wave is the '*main wave*' which in severe quakes can be seen as a ripple passing over the surface. This wave takes the longest route, around the outer layer of the crust, and arrives at the observatory some time after the other waves which pass through the Earth. The main wave is the one that causes the most damage.

A modified Mercalli Scale for determining the strength of Earth Tremors.

1. *Imperceptible*: detected only by instruments.
2. *Very weak*: detected by sensitive people at rest.
3. *Weak*: loose objects may be disturbed slightly.
4. *Moderate*: rattling of doors and windows; some sleepers wake.
5. *Fairly strong*: most sleepers wake. Noticed out of doors. Bells ring.
6. *Strong*: furniture overthrown; cracking of plaster.
7. *Very strong*: some damage to buildings.
8. *Destructive*: walls crack, chimneys fall.
9. *Very destructive*: severe damage; some buildings destroyed.
10. *Devastating*: foundations, roads, pipes, etc. damaged.
11. *Catastrophic*: few buildings survive; fissures in ground.
12. *Major Catastrophe*: complete destruction; crumpling of ground.

Rocks under tension are likely to split along a fault plane *and the separated blocks may move against each other. The vibrations thus set up are transmitted as earthquakes.*

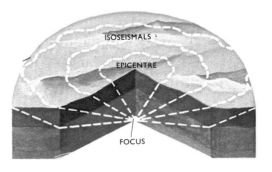

From the focus of a quake, vibrations spread out in all directions. The farther they travel, the weaker they become and so a number of zones are formed. The central ones experience more disturbance than the outer ones.

The distribution of the main earthquake regions corresponds closely to that of volcanic regions. In the Circum-Pacific and Mediterranean belts they are associated with recent mountain building; the Mid-Atlantic Ridge is an area of outwelling magma associated with rifting and fissuring.

CHAPTER TWELVE

How Mountains are Made

THE emergence of a mountain chain involves a great deal of disturbance of the Earth's crust. It is not a sudden event but the culmination of a long sequence of happenings which is called the *Orogenic Cycle* or the Cycle of Mountain Building. The crust of the Earth can be divided into two parts. First there is an upper layer that varies in thickness from next to nothing under the deep oceans to about 20 miles thick under the highest mountain ranges and about 7 miles thick under the plains near sea level. This part (the *sial*) is granitic in composition and has a density of about 2·7 times that of water.

The lower part of the crust (the *sima*)

is made up of dark basaltic types of rock which are about 3 to 3·4 times as dense as water.

Although the sima is strong and rock-like it acts as if it were a fluid and the less dense sial 'floats' on it. When anything floats in a liquid there is a balance between the height, or amount of material above the surface of the liquid and the amount below. Icebergs are good examples of this equilibrium which is called *isostasy*. The granitic masses try to keep an isostatic balance when floating on the basaltic layer. Continual erosion, plus the rigidity of the rocks concerned, however, make it impossible for a perfect equilibrium to be maintained,

54

though adjustments are continually being made. The coast of Norway and the islands of the Hebrides, for example, have risen by many feet during the last few thousand years as is shown by the presence of *raised beaches*. This is probably an adjustment for the disappearance of the huge weight of ice that was present during the Ice Ages.

The Mountain Building or Orogenic Cycle

The first stage in the cycle is the formation of a large, slowly sinking area of sea bed. The sediments brought down by rivers and floods from the land are laid down in the developing trough so that the area never becomes too deep nor does it silt up completely. During the early stages of this sinking there may be a considerable amount of volcanic activity, helped by weaknesses in the warped crust, so that the sediments often have lava flows and volcanic ashes mixed up with the other material. This type of trough is called a *geosyncline*, a name which indicates its trough-like nature as well as the large area that it covers.

While the trough is filling, all the land masses from which the sediments came are getting lighter and so isostatic balances need to be adjusted. The basalt layer beneath the land masses pushes upwards and lifts them. More sediment is then made available for deposition in the geosyncline.

For many millions of years the first phase can continue, but sooner or later the piling up of the basaltic layer at the sides of the geosyncline, together with the need for isostatic balance under the sediments in the trough lead to the onset of the second stage.

The second stage of mountain

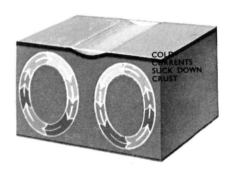

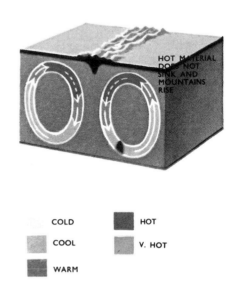

COLD   HOT

COOL   V. HOT

WARM

Diagrams to illustrate the theory of a geosyncline formation.

building is the compression of the sides of the geosyncline. The enclosed mass of rock is folded and buckled, the lowest sediments being squeezed into a 'root' for the mountain mass and the upper rocks being lifted out of the sea and forced to overlap the sides of the geosyncline, riding out over the compressing rocks in great overthrusts. The main uplift, however, is a later movement which restores the isostatic balance, the mountain range, with its deep root, rising slowly from the sima. The gradual changes taking place in the second stage cause a new area of subsidence to occur at the sides of the old geosyncline and the new mountain mass starts to erode and fill in these new areas in the same way as in stage one. This is the third stage of the cycle. This repetition of the cycle may occur two or three times before the whole *orogenesis* is complete.

Causes of Orogenesis or Mountain Building

The existence of the enormous forces needed to cause the downwarping of the crust over thousands of square miles and to buckle and fold rocks, as well as lift them to great heights calls for some explanation. Many theories have been put forward. It used to be thought that the cooling of the Earth was the main cause of mountain folding by reason of contraction, but that could not explain the continued action now.

The most likely cause of orogenesis would be convection currents within the Earth. The lower crust acts like a fluid, and the same is true of the mantle rocks below the crust. If there is a hotter area deep within the Earth there will be a rising current of hot, molten rock. This would be extremely slow because the rocks, though acting like fluids, are harder than steel and so the current would take centuries to move round. Although so slow, these currents would still exert a terrific force on the crust above. As a result, where two such currents met in the cooler areas and turned down towards the core of the Earth again they would tend to 'suck' down the surface and so cause a trough to develop. This would become the geosyncline. Eventually, as the areas of relatively hotter material shifted to other parts, the current would gradually lessen and stop. This would enable isostatic balance to be readjusted (as in stage two of the orogenesis). Thus the mountain ranges would rise like scum on the top of very thick, boiling jam.

Example of Orogenic Areas

The explanations given here are based on detailed study of many mountain ranges and most suitably explain the known facts. In the earliest days of the Palaeozoic Era (the first of the great ages of fossils) a geosyncline developed over much of what is now Wales. More than 30,000 feet of deposits built up over many millions of years. Most of the deposits were clearly laid down in shallow water thus proving the subsidence of the trough. All the stages can be traced in the types of

Floating ice-bergs illustrate the principle of isostasy. *The more there is above the water, the greater the volume below.*

Wrong as of 1977

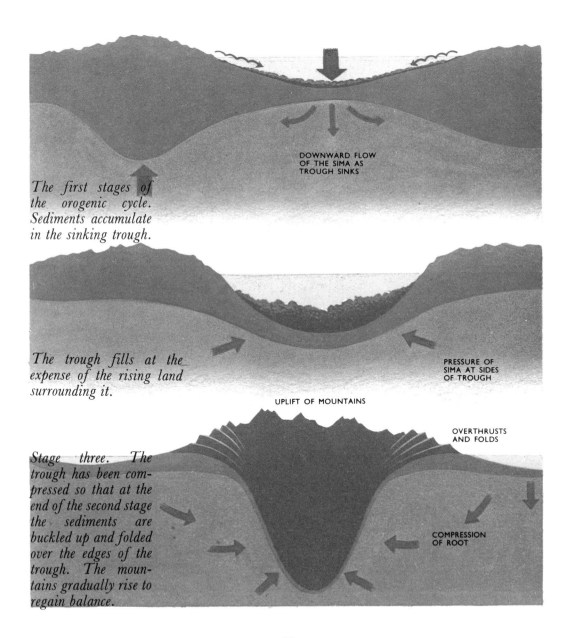

Mountain ranges and lowland plains behave in the same way as large and small ice-bergs and tend to 'float' on the denser material below.

The first stages of the orogenic cycle. Sediments accumulate in the sinking trough.

The trough fills at the expense of the rising land surrounding it.

Stage three. The trough has been compressed so that at the end of the second stage the sediments are buckled up and folded over the edges of the trough. The mountains gradually rise to regain balance.

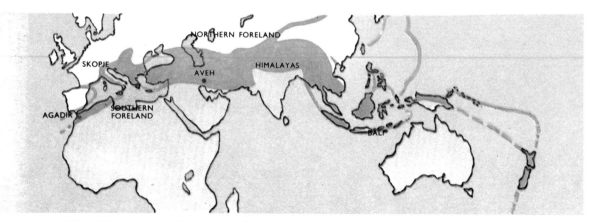

The Alpine orogenesis is marked and the positions of many recent earthquakes and volcanoes show how unstable the southern foreland is.

rock found (mostly slates, sands and grits) and all the volcanic areas can be traced. The final stage was the formation of the Welsh mountains, originally much larger than they are today.

The most recent of the mountain areas to be built was the great system of mountains that stretch right across Europe and through the Himalayas and down to the Java Sea. This last mountain-building episode is often called the *Alpine Orogenesis* because it has been studied most carefully in the Swiss Alps.

This orogenic area is still active in places. Where the mountains overthrust southwards into Africa, Italy, Greece, Iran and the East Indies there are still many earthquakes and volcanoes. The recent tragedies of Agadir, Skopje, and Bali are all along this front of the old geosyncline. Furthermore, the area is bordered by a geosyncline in the island area of the East Indies.

If all recent earthquakes were to be marked on a map of the world and compared with the mountain ranges the truth of the statement that the Alpine orogenesis is still with us would be amply borne out.

CHAPTER THIRTEEN

Continental Drift

AS early as 1620 it was noticed that the continents of Africa and Europe on one side of the Atlantic and the Americas on the other side would fit together like the pieces of a jigsaw if they were to be moved together. The 'nose' of Brazil would fit snugly into the Gulf of Guinea, the 'bulge' of West Africa would tuck into the Caribbean while North America would, with a little juggling of the pieces, lie fairly comfortably along the coast of western Europe.

It was only a very short step from noticing these complementary shapes to conceiving the idea that at one time they *had* been joined together. The first person to put forward this seemingly preposterous notion, Antonio Snider in 1858, used it as a means of explaining the similarity between fossils found in the Coal Measures of both North America and Europe. But lacking the backing of any scientific evidence it was quickly dismissed as a fanciful and fantastic notion.

It is interesting that, although the complementary shapes of the opposing lands of the Atlantic inspired the idea of continental drift in the first place, this is not a weighty argument in its favour. The continental shelves of the western part of the Old World and the eastern coast of the New are, of course, sialic, and if the continental shelves of S. America and Africa were brought together they would not necessarily fit perfectly. The similarity of the coastlines of the American and African continents may be pure coincidence; there is no clear evidence of sial in the deep Atlantic Ocean or on the Mid-Atlantic Ridge.

The idea was not brought up again until the beginning of the present century when two people, working quite independently, put forward theories of continental drift within two years of each other. In 1908 F. B. Taylor used the idea to explain the formation and distribution of the great fold mountain ranges of the present day. He supposed that the continents were originally grouped in two great land masses—Laurasia in the north and Gondwanaland in the south—and that these two masses spread out towards the equator. As Laurasia drifted southwards its leading edges were rumpled into mountain ranges while splitting in the rear produced the complex group of islands in northern Canada. And as Gondwanaland in the south drifted northwards. it broke into a number of pieces, forming Antarctica, South America,

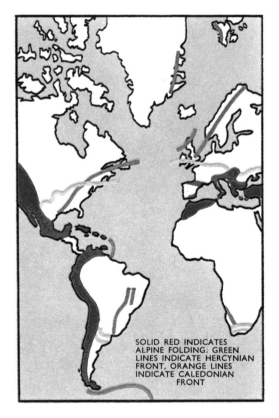

SOLID RED INDICATES ALPINE FOLDING. GREEN LINES INDICATE HERCYNIAN FRONT. ORANGE LINES INDICATE CALEDONIAN FRONT

The fold mountain belts of the opposing continents match very well. The meeting of the Caledonian and Hercynian fronts, forecast in Europe, is completed in North America.

Australia, India and Africa. Once again the leading edges of these drifting land masses were rumpled into mountain ranges.

Taylor supposed the two great land masses to have existed in Cretaceous times and to have broken up since then. But then the formation of the many great mountain ranges which were uplifted before this time could not be explained. His choice of the cause of continental drift was unfortunate too. He suggested that the Moon became a satellite of the Earth in Cretaceous times and it was then much nearer to the Earth than it is at present. The strong gravitational pull of the young Moon produced tidal

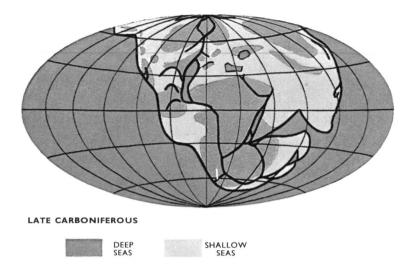

LATE CARBONIFEROUS

DEEP
SEAS

SHALLOW
SEAS

EOCENE

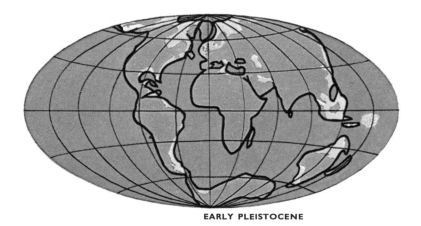

EARLY PLEISTOCENE

Wegener's three maps illustrating continental drift. The latitude of the various continents is purely arbitrary.

60

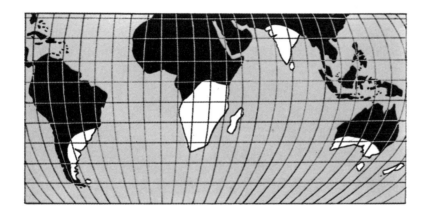

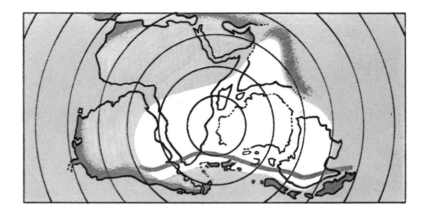

(upper left) Map showing the extent of the areas glaciated in Carbo-Permian times. Generally speaking, the ice advanced from the south. (upper right) Map showing the continents reassembled around the South Pole – the only way in which the extent of the Carbo-Permian glaciation can be explained.

forces on the Earth which dragged the continents away from the poles. But if the tidal forces had been that strong they would have braked the Earth to a standstill within a very short space of time.

In 1910 Alfred Wegener put forward his conception of continental drift and amassed a considerable amount of evidence to back it. Wegener was primarily a meteorologist and continental drift to him was, in the first place, a means of explaining the great climatic changes that have taken place in the past. A wealth of undeniable evidence points to the fact that the land masses have in the past experienced climates which would seem impossible if they were then in their present positions. Coal, for instance, which is formed from luxuriant, swampy, tropical forests, is found as far afield as North America, Europe, northern Asia and even icy Antarctica, none of which have a tropical climate at present. Other evidence of changing climates lies in past ice sheets.

61

During late Carboniferous or early Permian times the southern continents were partly covered with ice. Glacial deposits dating from this ice age have been found in South America, Africa, southern Australia and India and generally speaking the ice sheets advanced from the south in each case. This is evidence for continental drift, for it is impossible to imagine the existence of ice sheets which could embrace much of the southern continents and India at the same time, i.e. spread across the equator. The only explanation is that the glaciated continents were, at the time, grouped together to the south of their present positions.

The evidence assembled by Wegener covered a wide field. He drew up an impressive list of similarities between the opposing lands of the Atlantic covering earth movements, geological succession and fossil flora and fauna. A map shows how the fold mountain belts of the two continents match extremely well (though there are discrepancies in the time at which the most intense folding took place). Geological evidence in fact suggests that the opposing lands of the Atlantic

had a very similar geological history throughout the Palaeozoic and Mesozoic Eras.

Wegener supposed that the continental masses formed two blocks, a southern one equivalent to Gondwanaland and a northern one equivalent to Laurasia, separated from the start by a wide sea (Tethys). Despite the division, both blocks, according to Wegener, formed one great unit—Pangaea. This existed in early Carboniferous times but began to split up in Cretaceous times, the rift starting in the south and working northwards, so that the fracture opening up the Atlantic occurred as late as the Pleistocene Epoch (this began about one million years ago).

Wegener recognized two directions of movement, one towards the equator and the other westwards, due to complicated gravitational and tidal forces. The drift towards the equator was responsible for the creation of the Himalayas and Alps, which were squeezed between the closing jaws of Africa and India on one side and Eurasia on the other. The westwards drift is shown in the Andes and Rockies of the Americas which were

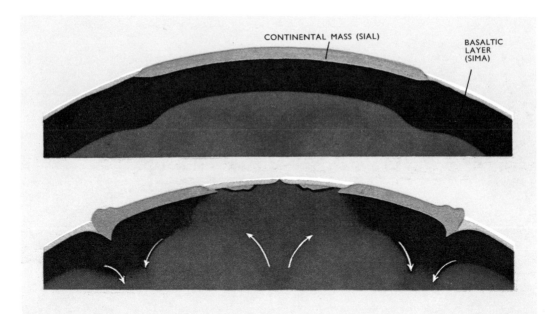

CONTINENTAL MASS (SIAL)

BASALTIC LAYER (SIMA)

One recent suggestion as to the cause of continental drift is a system of sub-crustal convection currents. This dispenses with the problem of how solid rock (the continents) came to be moved through solid rock (the sima). For the sima itself is carried along and the continents move with it. The diagrams illustrate how a system of convection currents could break up a great land mass such as Wegener's Pangaea and move the pieces apart. Mountains form where the sial of the continents tends to be dragged down by converging convection currents. The heavier sima is carried down and round in a great whirl by the currents. It eventually rises again and solidifies, healing the gaps in the outstretched crust.

(*left*) Mesosaurus, *a river-dwelling reptile of late Carboniferous times, has been found in both South America and South Africa – but nowhere else.*
(*below*) *The present-day distribution of various types of scorpions can only be explained satisfactorily by means of continental drift.*

(upper left) The Carboniferous flora of Laurasia, well preserved in coal measures, differed little throughout the region. *(upper right)* The strange-looking mammal, the manatee, found in estuaries of South America and North Africa, has been put forward as evidence of a link between these two regions in the past.

rumpled up by the drifting. The tail of South America lagged behind to form the 'horn'.

An important feature of Wegener's theory was that the geographical poles have wandered a great deal through geological time (in Carboniferous times the South Pole is placed off the coast of South Africa). Thus the drift towards the equator or 'flight from the poles' has changed from time to time according to position of the poles. In this way earlier mountain building is accounted for.

The forces suggested by Wegener as reponsible for continental drift, though real, are far too minute to drag solid rock through solid rock for thousands of miles. In fact *no* external force could do this without entirely disrupting the spin of the Earth. The continents are indeed great floating plates of solid rock but the material in which they are floating (the sima) is very solid too. A recent suggestion as to, the cause of continental drift gets around both of these difficulties (the force responsible for, and the movement of, solid rock through solid rock) by a system of convection currents beneath the Earth's crust. In this process the actual basaltic layer upon which the continents rest is carried along by sub-crustal convection currents and the continents move *with* it rather than *through* it.

The Shaping
of the Land

CHAPTER FOURTEEN

Weathering

HOWLING winds, lashing rain, ocean breakers, rivers in spate and creeping glaciers—these are the mightiest examples of the forces which wear away the land. Moving water and ice and wind are the tools of *erosion*; they eat away the land and transport the debris away. But there are other, more insidious processes at work which 'soften up' the crustal rocks, causing them to rot and disintegrate. These are collectively termed *weathering*. Their action is to break down relentlessly the solid rock of the Earth's crust and prepare a mantle of rock waste which can easily be removed by the tools of erosion. The soil itself is the best example of weathering. Basically, this is just broken-down rock which is waiting to be transported away.

There are two types of weathering, mechanical and chemical. Water and ice play an important role in mechanical weathering, and although it is difficult to make a clear distinction they are only classed as tools of erosion when in *motion*. Frost shattering is a process most conspicuous on exposed mountain slopes in temperate or cold climatic regions where it results in the formation of *screes* composed of angular fragments of rock of different sizes. When water turns to ice its volume increases by almost 9% and the force behind the expansion is tremendous, amounting to 2,000 pounds per square inch. Thus, water seeping into cracks in rocks and freezing tends to split the rocks apart.

Weathering in arid latitudes is largely due to the great range of day and night temperatures. Intensely heated during the day, the outer layers of a rock tend to pull away from the central mass, while during the cold night the rock loses its heat and contracts, causing more cracks to develop. In this way flakes are gradually detached from the main rock. Under certain conditions con-

Drastic changes in temperature may split pebbles cleanly in two.

66

Soil is basically a product of weathering.
Roots help to break down the solid rock.

Screes, composed of angular fragments of
rock, are the product of 'frost shattering'
on steep mountain slopes.

67

This split boulder shows the power behind a growing plant.

centric shells may peel off the rock, a process that is known as *exfoliation*, or, more descriptively, *onion weathering*. Coarse-grained rocks, such as granite, may simply disintegrate into their constituent minerals (because each expands a different amount) while pebbles are often split cleanly in two.

Life also helps in the process of destruction. Tree roots, for instance, grow down into cracks in the rock beneath and gradually widen them. The power behind a growing plant is quite remarkable; trees have been known to split gradually massive boulders in two. Burrowing animals such as earthworms also play their part by bringing to the surface fine material which can easily be washed away by rain. And in many parts of the world soil erosion bears witness to the fact that man himself has played no mean part in the destruction of the land by ignorant or careless farming methods.

Mechanical weathering is most evident in cold or arid regions, though it goes on all over the world. Similarly, chemical weathering is the most active process in moist climates,

WATER SEEPS INTO A CRACK IN A ROCK......

.....UPON FREEZING IT EXPANDS.......

.....AND THE ROCK IS SPLIT APART

68

especially where it is hot into the bargain. Chemical weathering is largely due to the action of rainwater which has dissolved carbon dioxide from the atmosphere, forming a weak solution of carbonic acid. This has a tremendous power to dissolve or alter the rock substance. In fact, practically the only common minerals which can withstand decomposition by carbonated water are quartz and muscovite. The calcium carbonate of limestone, for instance, is easily dissolved by rainwater, as is readily shown by the pitted, furrowed surface of many limestone platforms. Clay minerals result from the decomposition of felspars (an abundant group of minerals which are important constituents of igneous rocks). The action of rainwater on rocks rich in felspars results in the formation of clay, sand and carbonates. Another facet of chemical weathering is oxidation. This is due to the fact that rainwater also contains dissolved atmospheric oxygen. Oxidation is most marked in rocks containing iron compounds which take on red, brown or yellow tints.

In humid regions chemical weathering proceeds at a rapid pace and the rocks may be rotted more than one hundred feet below the surface. The common end product of weathering in tropical regions is laterite, a red, clay-like substance, which is a mixture of hydrated aluminium and ferric oxides.

In industrial cities there is evidence of chemical weathering induced by man. The eating away of tombstones and carved figures on buildings is largely due to the presence of sulphur dioxide in the air as the result of combustion processes. Dissolved in rainwater, this gas forms a weak solution of sulphurous acid.

The chemical weathering of limestone surfaces may produce a weird pattern of grooves and hollows.

Stalactites and stalagmites illustrate the process of solution. They are formed by the evaporation of ground water which has dissolved calcium carbonate from the limestone through which it has passed.

The eating away of stone carvings in industrial cities is largely due to air pollution.

69

CHAPTER FIFTEEN

The Agents of Erosion

EVER since the continents and the oceans were created there has been an unending battle between the land and the sea. In some places the land gains an advantage as it is uplifted by earth movements or new mountains are created. In other places the sea makes new inroads as ocean waves batter away at the coastline and rivers strip material from the land. But neither side can ever win. As soon as land is uplifted from the sea, wind, water and ice start their task of levelling. But the material which is deposited on the sea bed only goes to make more rock layers which will ultimately be uplifted to form more dry land.

The eating away of the land surface by moving water, ice and wind is closely linked with the process of weathering, for the agents of erosion not only wear away the land themselves but also carry away the products of weathering. *Denudation* is the term used to describe the combined effects of both destructive processes.

Some of the most striking effects of erosion are to be seen in arid regions where sharp grains of sand carried by the wind are blasted against fixed rocks, gradually smoothing them off and sometimes producing fantastic shapes. This is known as *wind abrasion*. The sand grains themselves are also smoothed down as they are dashed against rocks, time and time again, a process known as *attrition*. Even by itself the wind contributes a great deal to the destruction of the land, for

A narrow steep-sided valley, typical of the upper course of a river.

A natural arch results when two caves being excavated in the opposite sides of a headland unite.

it can remove unconsolidated (loose) material such as fine earth or sand. This is a great menace in semi-arid regions where the land has been ploughed for farming and the soil is no longer bound together by vegetation. In the notorious Dust Bowl of Kansas, U.S.A., during periods of drought, the wind has been known to strip whole farms completely of top-

Owing to the fact that some rock layers are softer than others weird shapes can be produced by wind abrasion.

The action of rain upon boulder clay may result in the formation of earth pillars. The boulders protect the material immediately beneath them from erosion and as the surrounding material is worn away they are left perched on top of a clay pillar. Ultimately, the stone cap falls off and the pillar is then rapidly washed away.

soil in a single night.

The might of the sea is contained in its waves. The force behind an ocean breaker is quite tremendous; during the winter it averages over 2,000 pounds per square foot and in storms it may exceed 5,000 pounds per square foot. It is not surprising, therefore, that the waves themselves can hammer down breakwaters by sheer weight of water. Once a crack appears in the rock it is rapidly widened as the water pounds into it and compresses trapped air. But far more damage is done by loose stones and boulders, which the waves hurl against the fixed rocks like battering rams. Cliffs result from the under-cutting action of the waves which carve a notch back into the base of the rock until the material above collapses, exposing a bare rock face.

Moving ice plays a considerable role in the sculpturing of the land. Striated (scratched) rocks, U-shaped valleys with truncated spurs, gouged rock basins and fiords – the unmistakable signs of glacial erosion – are to be found in many parts of the world. It may seem strange that moving ice can erode rock which is much harder than itself. Part of the answer lies in the boulders and pebbles which, gripped firmly by the ice, turn a moving glacier into a giant piece of 'sandpaper', with the ability to smooth and deepen the valleys through which it passes. But even pure ice can erode. Frozen into the ice, and thus held in a firm grip, whole blocks may be torn from a rock face as a glacier moves along (a process known as *plucking*). Glaciers also act as giant bulldozers, pushing large amounts of rock and soil ahead of them.

Running water is by far the most destructive of the agents of erosion. In fact it does more damage than all the rest put together (though this may not be true of a single area, *e.g.* a desert). The action of rain falling upon the land is to wash loose particles to lower levels. Under certain conditions this process can produce a landscape described as

Stones and boulders, firmly embedded in the ice, turn a moving glacier into a giant piece of sandpaper.

badlands, where the sloping ground is gashed into innumerable gullies and ravines.

Fed by rainwash, and eroding more material on their own account, streams and rivers carry vast quantities of material off the land. The Mississippi River alone dumps over one and a half million tons of rock debris into the Gulf of Mexico *every day*. All told, running water is lowering the drainage areas of the world at the rate of about one foot in ten thousand years. This may not seem a very impressive rate at first glance, but it must be remembered that thousands of years are mere minutes in the grand scale of geological time.

The erosive work of a river is accomplished in a number of com-plementary ways. In the first place there is the hydraulic action of the water alone which, when travelling at speed, can prise out large boulders. Then there is the corrosive action, due to chemicals contained in the water which are able to dissolve certain minerals from the rocks of the stream bed. Lastly there is *corrasion*, the wearing away of the stream sides and bed by impact with fragments in transport. Generally speaking corrasion is the most active process and a river's power of corrasion increases with its rate of flow. Thus erosion proceeds most rapidly in the upper reaches of a river where the gradient is steepest, and results in the creation of deep, steep-sided valleys.

CHAPTER SIXTEEN

The Work of Rivers

THE rain and snow that falls upon the land may follow a number of routes before it eventually returns to the atmosphere. A great deal is eva-porated as and where it falls; some is absorbed by plants and given off as water-vapour; some seeps further into the ground and adds to the *ground-water*. The rest (*surface run-off*) runs over the ground and finds its way to the sea by way of rivers.

Run-off is obviously greatest in hilly regions. Water running on the slopes is channelled into gullies by irregularities of the surface. The gullies join up and form small streams. At first, these flow intermittently, but as they remove soil and rock particles they soon cut down to the water-table (surface of the ground-water)

and permanent streams develop.

On the steep slopes the running water moves quickly and can rapidly deepen the channel and remove the resulting debris. The river water dissolves some of the rock material but this is not of much consequence in deepening the stream-bed. The power of the gushing water is sufficient to prise up loose boulders from the bed and banks. This in itself lowers the bed but even more important is the *corrasive* action of the stones and boulders. These rocks, trundled along by the current, quickly wear down the stream-bed. *Pot-holing* is a special case of corrasion: swirling eddies make depressions in the rocky bed and these hollows get filled with stones. Continued swirling of these quickly deepens and widens the hole and, if neighbouring pot-holes join up, the bed may be lowered by a considerable extent. During the process of corrasion the stones and boulders themselves become worn down – eventually to a fine silt which is held in suspension. This is partly why clear mountain streams become cloudy lower down their course.

Rivers then carry their load in three ways: in *solution*, as *suspended* fine particles, and as the *bottom load* (the rolling and jumping stones and rock debris). The amount (*total load*) that a river can transport depends upon the velocity and volume of the stream flow. Even a small stream can carry vast amounts of debris when swollen by flood water.

Everywhere along the course of the river there is a minimum necessary gradient that will give sufficient velocity to transport the load at that point. The river wears down its bed continuously until this minimum gradient is achieved. Further down-cutting goes on very slowly. In the lower reaches of the river the volume of water is large and the necessary gradient is therefore lower. The curve of a typical river from source to mouth (*long profile*) thus flattens out towards the mouth. When the minimum slope is reached in all parts of the river, it is said to be *graded*. It is, however, rare for a complete river to reach the graded condition.

Many rivers can be divided into three regions: the *mountain tract*, the *valley tract*, and the *lowland* or *plains tract*. These are all stages in the develop-

An upland stream strewn with large boulders. Although these are now stationary they are easily moved along when the stream is swollen after heavy rain.

A typical young valley with over-lapping spurs formed as the stream runs round obstacles.

The water running round a bend exerts the greatest force at the outside (arrowed). The spurs are thus worn away and the bends move down-stream, widening the valley in the process.

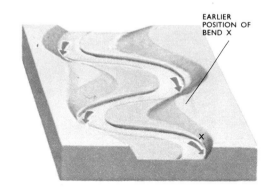

EARLIER POSITION OF BEND X

ment of the river. In some recently (geologically speaking) uplifted areas the mountain tract flows directly into the sea as a young and completely ungraded river. The processes whereby the swiftly-flowing mountain stream becomes a broad lowland river are best followed by studying the history of an imaginary stream.

When a region has been uplifted by some geological force, streams begin to flow on the slopes. These are *young* streams and they rapidly erode a channel through the rocks. If down-cutting is very rapid or if the rock is very resistant to weathering a steep-sided gorge may result. More frequently, however, the young stream flows in a V-shaped valley because the sides are worn down by rain, soil-

Pothole in a river bed caused by the swirling action of stones. If several holes join up they may lower the bed considerably.

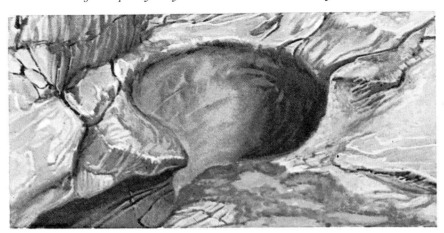

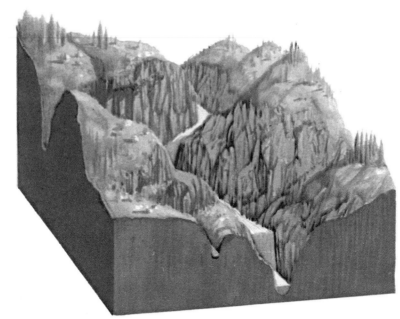

A young landscape showing swiftly flowing streams, waterfalls and steep sided valleys. (Left) The long profile of a young stream.

A mature landscape showing the rounded hills and gentle slopes. There is a small flood-plain. The profile shows that the river is graded above and below the falls.

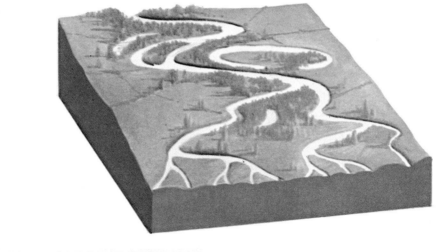

In old age the river has a very wide valley and the landscape is very flat. The river is completely graded.

erosion and land-slips. The running water seeks the easiest way down and its course is therefore irregular as it curves round obstacles. This leads to the formation of 'interlocking spurs' as the stream zig-zags down the slope.

When water runs round a curve it

Steep-sided gorges, such as this, result when the river cuts down rapidly and the rock is resistant to weathering.

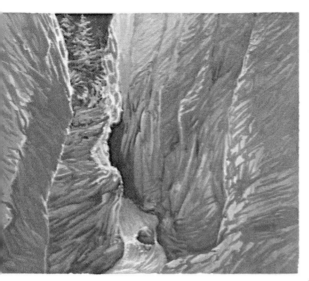

exerts its greatest force at the outside. The spurs and valley sides are therefore worn away at these points. On the inside of the bend, shingle is deposited. As the spurs and valley sides are worn away the river bends move downstream, cutting into the valley sides and the shingle deposits left by the previous bend. The valley is thus widened as well as deepened. The widening process goes on all the time, whenever the stream meets a slight obstruction and flows round it. The bends grow by erosion at the outside and push back the valley sides. During the course of this widening the river may become graded. The material eroded from the valley sides is deposited on the valley floor which becomes flat and forms the *flood-plain* The valley sides are smooth and served by tributary streams. This is the valley tract and the river and its valley are *mature* in this region. Further widening of the valley and flood-plain lead to the development of the plains tract and the beginning of old age.

As a whole, the river is now longer than at first, for while the original young stream matures it also grows back into the land by *headward erosion*. Soil-creep and landslips, at the source, wear back the rock and the 'young region' migrates inland. The young stream is normally ungraded and has an irregular slope. The irregularities must be removed before the graded condition is achieved. Small features are quickly eroded but rocks of differing resistance are serious hindrances to the grading process. They may form

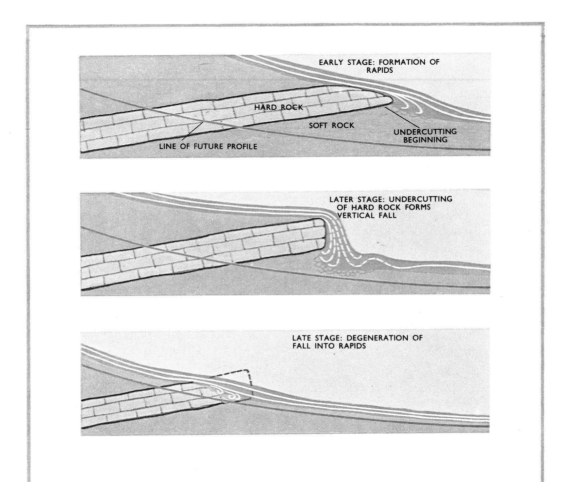

EARLY STAGE: FORMATION OF RAPIDS

HARD ROCK

SOFT ROCK

UNDERCUTTING BEGINNING

LINE OF FUTURE PROFILE

LATER STAGE: UNDERCUTTING OF HARD ROCK FORMS VERTICAL FALL

LATE STAGE: DEGENERATION OF FALL INTO RAPIDS

WATERFALLS

Where a hard band of rock is followed downstream by a softer one (such as shale or clay) the latter is worn away much more quickly and a steep slope results. The river runs down this as a *rapid*. Where the dip of the rock is such that the hard bed can be undercut a vertical face and a water fall can result. This fall must be removed before the river can reach the graded condition. As the water crashes over the fall it erodes the softer material and leaves hanging pieces of hard rock. These fall away and the falls recede upstream, leaving a gorge in front of them. Niagara Falls and many of the falls in the Yorkshire Dales are formed by limestone rock overlying softer shales.

As the falls recede they will reach a position where the base of the hard rock meets the future grading line. There will be no more undercutting and the falls will deteriorate into rapids and then disappear altogether.

high waterfalls or steeply sloping rapids, all of which must be reduced to the minimum slope. Large lakes, too, are a hindrance; they represent too shallow a gradient. It is common for a river to be mature and graded both above and below a large lake or fall, because the elimination of these takes so long.

Eventually the young stream may cut right back into land and meet another valley from the other side. There will be no more cutting back and the complete valley can reach maturity and grade. When the whole river is graded, downcutting is slow but it does go on. Because the land masses are much reduced there is less material carried down and the required gradient is less. The bed is therefore lowered towards base level. The ultimate result would be an almost flat plain (*peneplain*) with rivers meandering slowly over it.

Meanders are characteristic of rivers in the plains tracts or old age. They are sweeping curves that develop in all directions as the river meets any slight hindrance. At this stage the river is flowing entirely in its own deposits.

Old age is very rarely reached in a complete river. The time required would be enormous (millions of years) and Earth movements normally interrupt the cycle of erosion. Any uplift of the land produces sharp increases in slope and erosion is renewed – cutting back along the valley. The junction between the old and new slopes is called a *nickpoint*. Where the river cuts down into its own flood plain, *river terraces* are formed – flat ledges some way above the river. In time these disappear as the new valley widens out.

CHAPTER SEVENTEEN

The Work of Ice

DURING the Earth's long history the climates of the world have undergone many changes. But there have been few to match the change that took place less than $1\frac{1}{2}$–2 million years ago when temperatures fell, especially in the north, and the world entered the Great Ice Age. As more and more snow fell in winter and less and less melted in summer great ice sheets built up and moved slowly southwards across the land. At their greatest extent much of Asia, Europe and North America, more than eight million square miles in all, lay shrouded in ice. Lush sub-tropical regions were turned into icy wastes as Arctic conditions gripped the land and compressed the climates towards the equator. Like giant bulldozers the advancing ice sheets scraped the land clear of soil and dumped it farther south. They levelled forests, smoothed the tops off hills, scoured out valleys and carried huge boulders hundreds of miles from their parent outcrops to foreign resting places. The last glaciation ended about ten thousand years ago but vast tracts of land in the northern hemisphere still bear witness to the fact that moving ice can sculpture the land.

The rate at which a glacier can erode depends largely upon the speed at which it moves. Thus, the glaciers of Greenland, some of which move at

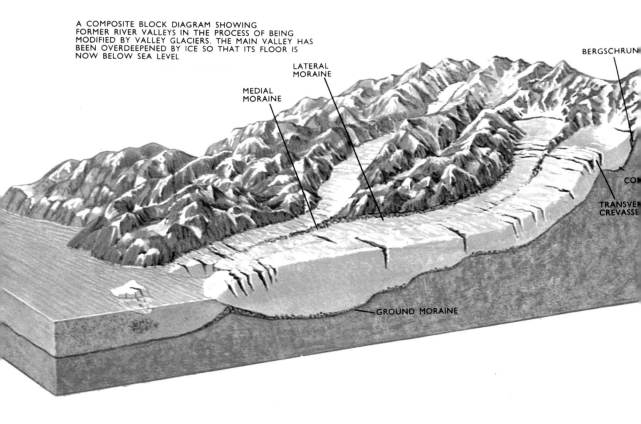

A COMPOSITE BLOCK DIAGRAM SHOWING
FORMER RIVER VALLEYS IN THE PROCESS OF BEING
MODIFIED BY VALLEY GLACIERS. THE MAIN VALLEY HAS
BEEN OVERDEEPENED BY ICE SO THAT ITS FLOOR IS
NOW BELOW SEA LEVEL

BERGSCHRUN

LATERAL
MORAINE

MEDIAL
MORAINE

CO

TRANSVE
CREVASSE

GROUND MORAINE

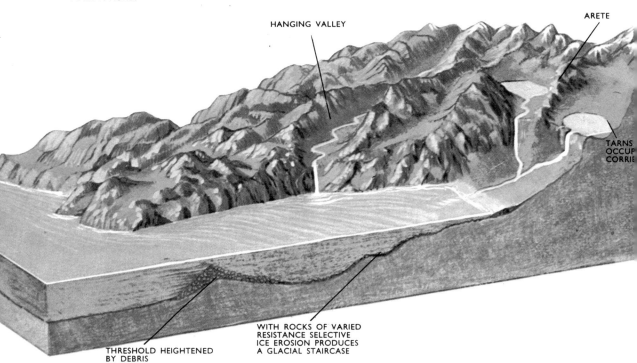

THE SAME LANDSCAPE AFTER THE GLACIERS HAVE MELTED AWAY.
THE SEA HAS INVADED THE OVERDEEPENED MAIN VALLEY TO
FORM A FIORD.

HANGING VALLEY

ARETE

TARNS
OCCUP
CORRIE

THRESHOLD HEIGHTENED
BY DEBRIS

WITH ROCKS OF VARIED
RESISTANCE SELECTIVE
ICE EROSION PRODUCES
A GLACIAL STAIRCASE

the rate of sixty feet per day, are many many times more destructive than those of the Alps which travel just a few feet per day. Hence, a continental ice sheet, which advances very slowly indeed, would do little more than smooth the existing landscape.

One of the most characteristic signs of glacial erosion is the U-shaped valley, with its flat boulder-strewn floor bounded by steep sides. These valleys are not entirely due to the action of glaciers; they were river valleys before the ice squeezed through them. Probably the most spectacular ice-shaped valleys are the fiords with their sheer bare rock walls towering above deep water. Glaciers were able to erode fiords below sea-level because ice needs to be almost submerged before it will float. But many fiords are fairly shallow near their mouth where a rocky bar or ridge, often capped with debris, rises from the valley floor almost to sea level. This *threshold* is due to a thinning in the depth of ice near the snout of the glacier.

Many glaciated valleys have water-falls tumbling down their sides from tributary valleys at a much higher level. These *hanging valleys*, which produce some of the highest waterfalls in the world, are probably due to the fact that size is a significant factor in a glacier's ability to erode the land. The glacier which occupied the main valley would have been much bigger than its affluents and consequently more destructive. Hence, when the ice melted, the floor of the tributary valleys would have been left at a higher level than the floor of the main valley, the difference between the two depending upon the difference in size of the glaciers which squeezed through them. But the complete explanation of hanging valleys may not be as simple as this. It has been suggested that the difference in floor level may be partly due to the fact that the tributary valleys contained glaciers after those in the main valleys had melted. Since running water is a more powerful agent of transportation than moving ice, the main valley containing a river would have been eroded more quickly than the tributary valleys containing glaciers. There is probably some truth in this, for tributary valleys facing away from the Sun (i.e. those which are likely to have contained glaciers the longest) are sometimes found to hang more than those on the opposite side of the main valley.

Another hallmark of glacial erosion is the *corrie*, also known as a *cwm* or *cirque*. This is a large hollow in a mountain side and is frequently found in glaciated highlands. Many are now occupied by small lakes but once they marked the head of valley glaciers. Corries have a tendency to work back up the mountain side as their walls are 'shattered' by frost and 'plucked' by moving ice. Sometimes it happens that two corries almost meet and the narrow wall of rock which then separates them is known as an *arête*. If there are corries all around a mountain they are likely to produce a pyramidical peak such as the Matterhorn.

Glaciation is not entirely a destructive process, for the material eroded in one place must eventually be dropped in another as the ice melts. The plains of England and northern Europe are literally plastered with boulder clay robbed from such places as Scandinavia (which to this day suffers from a lack of good soil). It is a similar story in North America

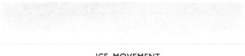

The elongated tapering ends of drumlins indicate the direction of ice movement.

Rocks carried great distances by glaciers are known as erratics. *If left in a precarious position, they are called* perched blocks.

(Below) A glaciated valley showing the typical U shape and truncated spurs.

where material scraped from Canada now provides fertile farmland in central U.S.A. *Boulder clay* or *till* is an unsorted mixture of debris of all kinds ranging from fine *rock flour* to great boulders weighing many tons. But the two main types are *basal till*, which is rich in clay, and *superglacial till*, which is more stony, much of the clay having been washed away by melt-water from the ice. Sometimes the boulder clay is plastered down as a collection of streamlined whale-backed mounds, usually less than a mile in length and rarely more than 200 feet high. These are *drumlins* and when grouped together they form what is aptly termed 'basket of eggs' topography.

The accumulations of rock debris which are carried and deposited by glaciers are called *moraines*. Boulder clay or till deposited from the underside of a glacier forms the *ground moraine*. *Lateral moraines* result from rock fragments falling on the sides of a glacier and when two glaciers meet the inner lateral moraines unite to form a *medial moraine*. Then, at the snout of a glacier, debris is piled up to form a *terminal moraine* if the ice front remains stationary long enough. Many of the world's lakes are caused by moraines acting as natural dams.

The melt-water from a glacier or an ice sheet plays its own part in erosion and deposition. *Eskers* are long winding ridges of sand and gravel which run roughly parallel to the direction of ice movement. The material is deposited by water which is confined to a narrow channel under the ice. Occasionally eskers have a beaded appearance, the beads marking the mouth of the subglacial stream during periods of ice-stand when the rate at which the glacier or ice sheet advanced was exactly balanced by the rate at which the ice melted back. *Outwash fans* show where the subglacial streams left their confined channel under the ice. A sudden checking of speed as the water spread out over the land resulted in the deposition of the material they were carrying. The erosive action of melt-water may be considerable when normal drainage is upset by ice and a new outlet channel has to be cut.

CHAPTER EIGHTEEN

The Work of the Wind

IN regions of moderate rainfall, wind erosion is of only minor importance. The land-surface is clothed with vegetation and, apart from controlling the distribution of rain and adding something to the power of waves, the wind has little effect on the rate of erosion. However, in the drier regions of the world, where rainfall is slight or is quickly evaporated, the wind plays a dominant part in the sculpturing of the land. About a fifth of the Earth's surface is covered by such desert regions, with little or no vegetation. The scanty rainfall is due to various climatic and geographic features.

Desert regions are usually subject to extreme temperature changes and bare rocks tend to shatter as a result. Because it is fully exposed, the loose material is easily blown about by the wind. The latter tends to blow from a fixed direction in any one desert region. The finest particles are carried a long way by the wind and are eventually deposited outside the desert area as *loess*. Outside the desert, this fine material is fixed by plants and is not blown further. Much of China is covered with loess which has been blown from the Asian deserts.

Conditions within the desert depend very much upon the types of rock present. Shales and limestones that contain very little or no silica do not provide sand grains, and the desert in this case is a mass of shattered rock. Where sandstones or certain igneous rocks are present, grains of sand (quartz), predominate in the shattered material. Weathering of mixed deposits such as alluvium or boulder clay also produces a good deal

Wind-blown sand attacks any weakness in rocks and is responsible for weird shapes such as this arch in Utah, U.S.A.

of sand. These sand grains play an important part in the further erosion of the land. The wind can carry them for short distances, and in doing so,

83

A typical *barchan* (crescent-shaped dune) formed by the wind.

Gravel beds in the desert are not permanent features. The action of wind-blown sand wears down the fragments on the upper surfaces so that a flat mosaic surface appears. Eventually the gravel is worn down to sand and other particles small enough to be blown away. Individual pebbles on the surface of the sand become characteristically shaped by the blast of sand grains. They become bevelled on the windward side, and, if they become displaced, two or more sides may be affected. The bevelled sides meet along sharp edges. These wind-shaped pebbles are called *ventifacts* or *dreikanters*.

hurls the grains at the rock with considerable force. Hard rocks come to stand out above softer ones as cliffs and isolated hillocks. Hard nodules and fossils in soft bands of rock stand out and eventually fall out. The erosive action of the sand grains is greatest just above ground level and undercutting of cliffs is very pronounced.

Continuous removal of the sand grains concentrates the larger fragments into gravel areas in the region of the exposed rocks. There are thus three types of surface: the bare rock, kept clear and polished by the continuous action of wind and sand; the gravel deposits; and the sand which accumulates wherever the wind drops to any extent.

During their abrasive work the sand grains themselves become very worn and eventually become quite rounded. **They are very different from the more angular grains laid down in water. The greater speed and the lack of a 'cushion' of water help to smooth**

wind-blown (*aeolian*) sands more than water-borne ones. Wind-blown sands also lack mica – the flaky mineral so common in water-laid deposits. These two features help to identify ancient sandstone formations as windborne or marine sands.

Sand that is picked up by the wind is not carried indefinitely. Whenever the wind speed drops, the sand is deposited. The slightest mound of sand will hinder the next wind and more sand will be deposited. A *dune* will be built up with a long windward slope and a steeper leeward slope. Dunes are often formed along exposed shores – for instance along the coasts of Holland and Northern France. In humid regions they are stabilized by

The windward slope of dunes is long. When the wind is not fully laden with sand it removes some from the windward side and deposits it over the face. The whole dune thus moves forward.

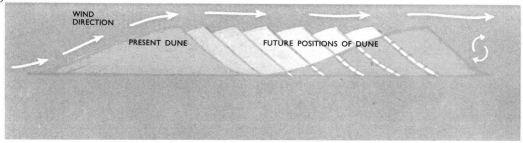

WIND DIRECTION

PRESENT DUNE   FUTURE POSITIONS OF DUNE

vegetation but in the desert they migrate under the influence of the wind. Sand on the windward slope is blown over the crest and so the dune moves forward.

The lateral edges of the dune are normally shallower than the central part and these side regions move forward more rapidly. Crescent shaped dunes called *barchans* (bar-cans) develop, and grow until the 'wings' have the same wind-resistance as the central part. The barchans then migrate as a whole. There are hundreds of square miles of shifting dunes and barchans in the Sahara. These have been formed during a very long period of erosion and accumulation of sand.

CHAPTER NINETEEN

The Work of the Sea

THE havoc created by severe storms at seaside resorts gives some idea of the power of the sea. In recent centuries, whole settlements have been destroyed on the east coast of Britain as the sea continued to attack the coast-line and destroy the cliffs. However, the eroded material must go somewhere and it is deposited at other points on the coast, effectively extending the land. This, then, is the work of the sea: erosion, transport and deposition. The work is controlled by a variety of factors all delicately balanced and it may take only a small change to convert an erosion coast into one of deposition or vice-versa.

Two basic types of coast-lines are recognised. These are the *submergent* and *emergent* coasts. Submergent coasts are very common at the present time for the sea-level has been rising since the last ice-age and flooding the coast-lines. Where the land's features run parallel to the coast, numerous islands and long inlets are formed upon submergence. This type of coast is the *Pacific* type and is well shown by the west coast of Yugoslavia. Where the structure is perpendicular to the coast, the latter is of the *Atlantic* type with long inlets and headlands. South

Wales and Southern Ireland show this feature very well. After submergence, erosion tends to exaggerate the features at first, but the inlets gradually become silted up and the headlands worn away until a regular coastal outline develops on mature coasts. Erosion then proceeds at a more or less uniform rate all along the coast.

Emergent coasts are not common at present. Raised beaches, salt marshes and flat-topped cliffs are associated with uplift of the land relative to sea-level.

The erosive power of the sea depends, not on currents, nor to any great extent on tides, but on the *waves*. Waves are undulations of the water

Submergent coastlines may be of Atlantic or Pacific types. These are well illustrated by the coasts of Southern Ireland (left) and Yugoslavia (right).

ATLANTIC   PACIFIC

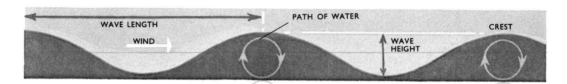

WAVE LENGTH

WIND

PATH OF WATER

CREST

WAVE HEIGHT

Waves in the open sea are disturbances of the water carried by wind. The water does not move forward in bulk but each particle at the surface describes a circular path as shown. These disturbances are transmitted to the deeper layers as smaller circular paths.

surface caused by the wind and they move forward in the direction of the wind. They start off in the open sea and increase in height and speed. The size depends upon the distance (*fetch*) over which the wind blows but the waves continue into regions well beyond the winds that formed them. It is, however, only the shape that moves forward, not the water itself. This is easily proved by watching floating objects: they ride up and down but do not move forward with the wave. The water travels on a circular path whose diameter is equal to the height of the wave from trough to

The erosive power of the sea is well shown here where boulder clay cliffs are being demolished.

crest. This movement sets up similar movements in the lower levels of water down to a depth corresponding approximately to the wave length. The latter is the distance from one crest to the next.

As the waves approach the shore and begin to disturb the sea-bed they are slowed down. Because of this feature, the waves tend to come in nearly parallel to the shore – if they start off obliquely, the inner part is slowed down first and the whole wave swings round parallel to the shore.

When the wave reaches water whose depth is about the same as the wave height, it can continue no longer and *breaks*. The breakers surge forward over the beach as *surf*, and then back down the beach as *back-wash*.

As the breakers and on-shore currents bring the surface-waters on to the beach an off-shore current (the undertow) flows away from the beach. This current returning the water to the sea is sometimes very strong and a danger to swimmers.

Marine Erosion

There are several ways in which the sea wears down the land. The power of the breakers as they crash upon the land is sufficient to crack and shatter many rocks. When cracks open up, water is forced in under high pressure and compresses trapped air. The effect is just like blasting and the rocks break up. By cutting into the land, the waves create overhangs in the rocks which gradually break off and develop into cliffs. This is the hydraulic action of the water.

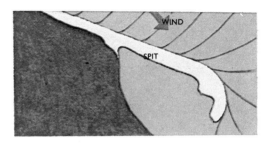

Longshore drift continues in a line when the coast turns in at a bay or estuary. Spits *are thus formed across the bay.*

The rock boulders and pebbles broken from the cliffs are picked up by the waves and thrown at the rocks and then dragged back along the shore. This, too, adds to the effect of the water and is known as *corrasion*. It must not be confused with *corrosion*, which is the chemical action of the water on the rock. The pebbles and boulders themselves gradually become rounded and worn down by continuous movement. This process is called *attrition*.

The rate at which cliffs are cut back depends upon their hardness and upon

Caves formed on each side of a headland may unite and produce a natural arch (left). Collapse of the roof leaves a stack *(right).*

87

Lulworth Cove, Dorset – a classic example of marine erosion in rocks of varying hardnesses.

The diagram shows how Lulworth Cove was formed by the breaching of the limestone and the erosion of the softer clays.

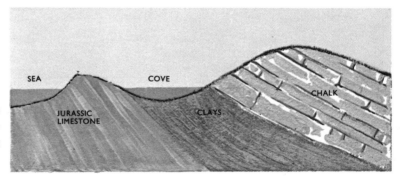

the amount of debris that remains at their base. Soft rocks, such as the boulder clays of North-East England, are worn back very rapidly. The coast has receded more than two miles since Roman times. Granites and limestones are resistant and wear back much more slowly.

As the waves cut back the cliffs they form a *wave-cut platform* at the base. The debris is swept to and fro on this platform and gradually wears it down so that a gentle slope is formed. The wider this platform becomes, the more it slows down the waves and thus the more it protects the cliffs behind. Such a platform can develop only where there are hard rocks.

Bays develop where soft rocks such as clays and shales are being eroded. Hard rocks stand out as headlands for a time but gradually the forces of erosion and deposition combine to form a smoother coastline. When headlands stand out beyond the rest of the coast they receive the full force of the sea's power and are worn back fairly rapidly. Caves frequently develop in limestone and other rocks. If two caves unite, a natural arch will be

Longshore drift is well shown by the heaping of shingle against the windward sides of groynes.

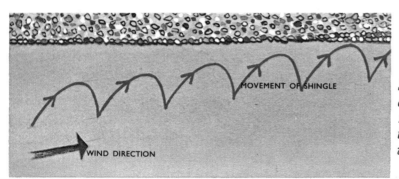

Surf and backwash combine to move in a zigzag in the direction of the prevalent winds.

formed. Collapse of the upper part leaves a *stack* standing some way from the cliffs.

Transport and Deposition of Eroded Material

As the waves cut into the coast and remove the rock material, they carry the latter to and fro on the wave-cut platform and beyond. The debris consists of large and small boulders, sand and silt. Breakers coming on to the beach bring the debris with them and deposit it. The back-wash however is very weak and can carry back only the finer material, thus pebbles and shingle come to occupy the upper shore, followed lower down by sand and the silt. Heavy storms and high tides carry shingle far up the shore and deposit it as a *storm beach*. The latter has great value in protecting the coast from further erosion. In time the beach becomes adjusted so that at each point the slope is just sufficient for the backwash and under-tow currents to carry away the material received with each breaker. Off-shore dredging may seriously upset the balance and whole beaches have been removed by the sea in order to regain its equilibrium. This can lead to serious erosion of the coast again.

It is well known that sands and gravels move along the coasts as well as up and down the beaches. The famous Chesil Beach of Dorset in England contains many pebbles from Devon and Cornwall. This movement along the shore is called *long-shore drift*. It is partly due to currents on the continental shelf but mainly due to wave action. Only rarely do waves come in quite parallel to the beach, they are usually slightly oblique. The back-wash however is straight down the beach so that the sand and gravel traces out a zig-zag line and moves along in the direction of the prevailing wind.

The existence of long-shore drift is well proved by the heaping of sand and shingle against the windward sides of the groynes that are built at some sea-side resorts. While the groynes may help to preserve the beach in the immediate neighbourhood this practice has sometimes caused severe damage further along the coast by starving those regions of the flow of shingle.

Where the coast-line is irregular, the long-shore drift may continue regardless of the shore-line, and in this way shingle spits develop across estuaries and bays. Waves or currents normally limit the growth of spits.

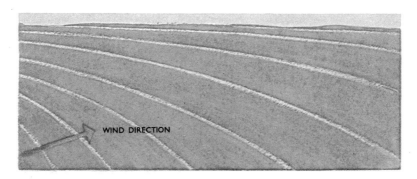

WIND DIRECTION

When a wave approaches the shore obliquely the inner end slows down first and the whole wave swings round and comes in nearly parallel to the beach.

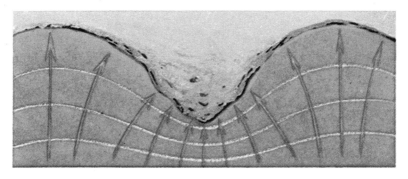

Wave action concentrates on the headlands of an irregular coast and tends to wear them down. A uniform outline will eventually be obtained if the rocks are of uniform hardness.

90

CHAPTER TWENTY

How Caves are Formed

NATURALLY-OCCURRING underground cavities are called caves – in distinction to tunnels and shafts which are man-made. Far more than just being intriguing 'holes in the ground', caves have brought a whole new field of science into existence – the science of *spelaeology* (Greek, *spelaion*, a cave).

Spelaeology embraces many scientific fields – geology, chemistry, physics and biology. The spelaeologist wants to know what the physical conditions are like underground, what organisms live there, what creatures formerly used the caves as shelters. But perhaps most fundamental of all, he wants to know just how caves have been formed.

The Formation of Caves

Every sort of rock contains openings. This property is called its *porosity*. The openings may be pore spaces between particles of sediment (*primary porosity*); or they may be fissures opened along planes of weakness (*secondary porosity*). The three planes of weakness important in cave formation are the *bedding planes* – lines of contact separating rocks of different composition and physical properties, *faults* – fractures in the crust along which slabs of rock have moved; and *joints* – fractures which have simply opened in rocks under stress.

It is the planes of weakness rather than the pore spaces which are important in cave formation. The openings are initially very small. But they become enlarged by natural agencies – either the sea or running water.

Formation of Sea Caves

The sea makes caves in all types of rock. Pounding waves beating against cliffs exploit the planes of weakness. The water rushing against the rocks traps air in the small openings already present. The air, enormously compressed, adds to the battering action

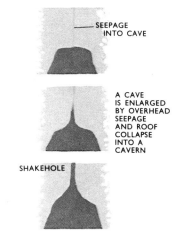

SEEPAGE INTO CAVE

A CAVE IS ENLARGED BY OVERHEAD SEEPAGE AND ROOF COLLAPSE INTO A CAVERN

SHAKEHOLE

Caves become enlarged by seepage and roof-fall into caverns (right). Complete roof collapse along a line of caverns may result in a dry limestone gorge. Left, the vertical-sided Cheddar Gorge, Mendip Hills, Somerset may well have been formed by just such a series of collapses.

of the waves and the rocks begin to disintegrate.

Any type of rock which outcrops at the coast is subjected to this treatment and caves can develop in all of them. However, the 'weak' rocks such as soft clays do not possess the necessary rigid strength and caves which begin to develop soon collapse. Larger, more enduring caves are cut into the harder rocks – sandstones, limestones, and igneous rocks – particularly where wave action is strong.

A rise in the level of the shore may mean that former shore-line caves are lifted high above their places of origin.

Formation of Inland Caves

The action of moving water through the rocks is the chief factor in the making of inland caves. It is the corrosive action of the water – its ability to dissolve the rocks it is passing through – which is of greatest importance. The mechanical erosion by the moving water does not have the same marked effects. Consequently, caves are rarely found in igneous rocks or sandstones. They are nearly all confined to limestone country.

Limestones are composed of at least 50% calcium carbonate, sometimes with a certain quantity of magnesium carbonate also present. Pure water does not have much effect on limestone. But in falling through the air, and especially in penetrating through surface layers of soil, rainwater becomes charged with carbon dioxide – it becomes a weak solution of carbonic acid. The carbonic acid reacts with the insoluble calcium carbonate, forming the soluble bicarbonate salt which is carried away.

Even so, not all limestones necessarily make good caving country. The limestone must be thick and receive a sufficient quantity of rain water. Next, the planes of weakness must be suitably arranged. Where joints and bedding planes are close together, too many openings are available and no single

Cave systems are not static. Changes are constantly occurring. Here a newly developed channel has by-passed an original passage, with the result that the original passage is no longer used. Left 'high and dry' it may over the years become encrusted with stalactites and other limestone deposits.

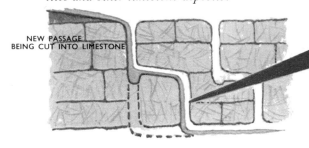

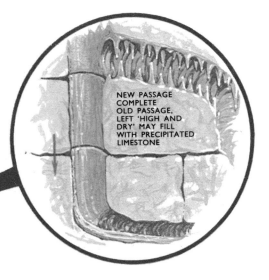

large passage develops. What is needed are well spaced planes with flow-off locally concentrated by favourable ground contours. By corrosion, funnel shaped cave entrances may develop – the *swallow* holes or *sink* holes.

In Britain the thick Carboniferous limestones are most suitable for cave formation, and in the U.S.A. these rocks (Mississippian) have produced the most extensive cave network yet discovered – the 150-mile-long Mammoth Hole system of Kentucky. Chalk, a very pure limestone, is too 'weak' and caves soon collapse.

Important in predicting just where caves are likely to develop in a limestone area is consideration of the water-table. Below the table, all cavities in the rock are permanently filled with water. This zone is called the *phreatic zone*. Above, rocks are not saturated – this is the *vadose zone*. Water simply passes through into the phreatic zone below.

The obvious place to expect caves to originate and develop is in the vadose zone. Water, charged with carbon dioxide, moves downwards under the influence of gravity. Paths followed may be along dipping bedding planes, or they may be down almost vertical joints (creating *potholes*).

In the phreatic zone water movement also takes place, though not nearly so fast as in the vadose zone. Water is finally discharged by seepage into seas or rivers. The movement is caused not so much by gravity as by hydrostatic pressure – the *water head*. The pressure arises because the water table at the points of outlet are at a lower level than elsewhere in the table. Flow against gravity may even occur for water may at times be moving at a lower level than the ultimate point of

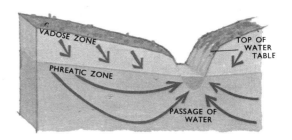

The vadose zone lies above the water table, the phreatic zone below. In the vadose zone movement is controlled by gravity. In the phreatic zone movement is caused by water pressure and channels are more horizontal and may even slope uphill.

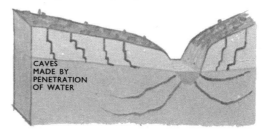

discharge. Caves originating in the phreatic zone generally follow more horizontal paths than in the vadose zone and may even slope up-hill.

Undoubtedly water flow in both zones has played a part in cave origin. By a lowering of the water table, however, either by a drier climate or by a nearby river cutting a deeper bed, the phreatic zone can become lifted into the vadose zone and the caves become modified by water moving directly under gravity.

A cave, by rock fall, may become very enlarged, in which instance it is called a *cavern*. Heavy falls of rock may, however, appreciably block an exit and the water becomes forced to flow out through another passage. The initial pattern may as a result become altered. Some roof collapses give rise to depressions in the ground above – the *shakeholes*. Extremely large scale collapses may actually form gorges.

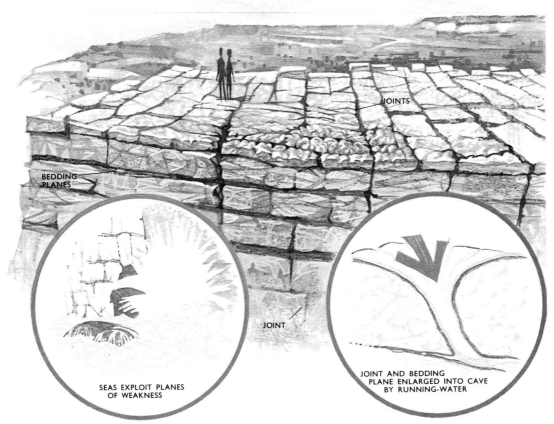

BEDDING PLANES

JOINTS

JOINT

SEAS EXPLOIT PLANES OF WEAKNESS

JOINT AND BEDDING PLANE ENLARGED INTO CAVE BY RUNNING-WATER

Limestone scarp showing bedding planes and joints. Such planes of weakness are exploited by weathering and caves may form. Inset – the sea and running water are the two important cave-forming agencies.

Structures in Caves

Pure water has little effect on limestone. Only between 20 and 74 parts per million of calcium carbonate by weight will be dissolved. In contrast, water containing carbon dioxide gas dissolves up to 400 parts per million. Some of the carbon dioxide comes from the atmosphere but far more is received when rain water seeps through the soil.

Thus, carbonated water may seep through the fissures and pores in the limestone, and quickly dissolve a quantity of lime. However, if the water should penetrate into a spacious cave in the vadose zone where carbon dioxide in the air is the same as in the atmosphere, then carbon dioxide is given off from the water and lime becomes deposited. Alternatively, because of draughts, the water droplet may evaporate again with the precipitation of limestone. This is, of course, the exact reverse of the corroding process.

Such precipitation in the spacious airy caverns of the vadose zone gives rise to the stalactites, stalagmites and frozen cascades. Many lesser known, more irregular, but equally beautiful structures may be formed as well.

94

The Wealth
of the Earth

CHAPTER TWENTY-ONE

Oil Geology

EVERY day millions of gallons of fuel oil are needed to power the world's machinery. Without this **immense supply, cars, aircraft, diesel** locomotives, many ships and all sorts of engines in work-shops and factories would be useless. Fuel oils are obtained from 'crude oil' – a mixture of organic chemicals formed within the Earth's crust over a period of many millions of years. Crude oil also provides Man with a source of natural gas, paraffins, alcohols and ketones – all important raw materials for the manufacture of a whole host of chemicals including plastics.

Almost certainly crude oil was formed from the remains of millions of minute animals and plants that drifted in the surface waters of ancient seas. When these organisms died, their remains sank down into deep, unaerated waters. Normally their soft parts would have been eaten by other creatures or broken down by bacteria into carbon dioxide and water. In the stagnant muds however this was prevented by the lack of oxygen. Instead, only a partial decomposition took place by the action of certain kinds of bacteria (*anaerobic* bacteria) which can survive without free oxygen. The anaerobic bacteria obtained the oxygen they needed from the dead tissues and left behind a mixture of organic chemicals rich in hydrogen and carbon – 'crude oil'. A similar first stage of oil formation is taking

A use of the seismic method in oil exploration. Shock waves caused by an explosion are reflected back to the ground from the surfaces between different types of rock. In the picture an anticlinal structure has been discovered.

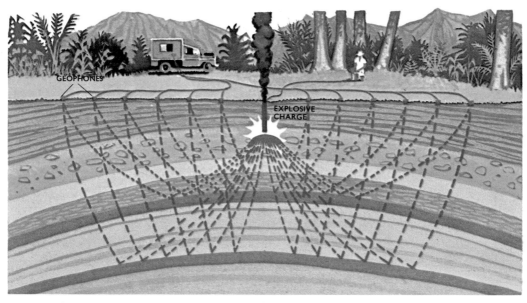

place today in the Black Sea and Caspian Sea. Sediments dredged up from the stagnant waters are already rich in certain hydrocarbons. Over millions of years, however, further chemical and bacterial reactions take place, probably influenced by the increase of temperature and pressure caused by the weight of overlying rocks.

Really the formation of oil is very similar to the formation of coal. The difference in composition of the two fuels is thought to be due only to differences in the nature of the organisms from which they are formed.

Coal is derived in the main from land plants very rich in carbon; oil is thought to be produced from the remains of tiny floating animals and plants which contain a high proportion of hydrogen in their fats, waxes and resins.

Most oil today is taken from marine deposits of less than 150 million years of age. The oil-bearing rocks of the U.S.A. are between 250 and 450 million years old. No oil is yet known from Cambrian and Pre-Cambrian sediments – rocks more than 500 million years old.

The remains of minute animals and plants accumulated in the muds of stagnant waters.
Inset. Microscopic view of the minute organisms.

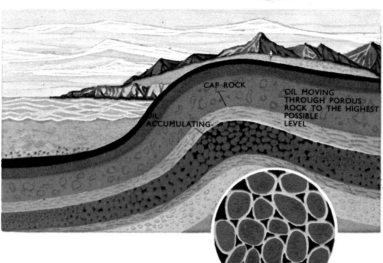

Pressures which fold the rocks and the weight of over-lying sediments forced the oil upwards through porous rocks.
Inset. Section of an oil-bearing sandstone; the oil can move in the space between the grains of sediment.

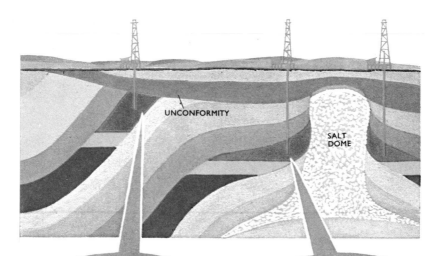

UNCONFORMITY

SALT
DOME

'Stratigraphic' trap. New sediments deposited on the weathered surface of older folded rocks have acted as a trap rock for the oil.

A salt dome pushes the overlying rocks upwards and may pierce them. Oil in the inclined porous layers is then trapped by the impermeable salt mass.

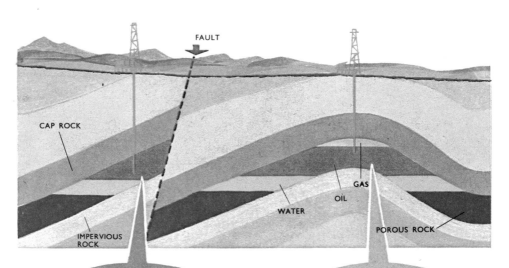

FAULT

CAP ROCK

GAS

OIL

WATER

POROUS ROCK

IMPERVIOUS ROCK

'Fault' trap. By movement along the fracture in the rocks, oil in porous sediment is brought against an impervious layer, and cannot escape.

'Anticlinal' trap. The oil in the porous layer has moved upwards to the highest point possible in the folded rock. The overlying layer prevents its escape.

Oil does not exist under the ground as pools of liquid. Instead, it is dispersed as droplets between grains of sediment. When an oil-well is first drilled, the pressure of water and natural gas within the oil-bearing rock drives these droplets into the bottom of the well. Usually the pressure is even great enough to force the oil upwards all the way to the surface. A spectacular example of this condition is the 'gusher' – a violent upsurge of crude petroleum which may occur if care is not taken to control a new well with suitable pressure valves.

No matter how great the natural pressure first was in an oilfield, it steadily becomes less and less. Oil accumulating at the bottom of the well is no longer driven to the surface but has to be pumped up mechanically or artificially forced up by driving down pressurized gas. In the very last stage of an oilfield's history, water and sometimes gas, is *injected* under pressure into the oil-bearing sands between the actual oil-producing wells. The residue of oil left between the grains of sediment is artificially driven into the wells and so recovered.

Oilfields

The weight of overlying rocks or the pressures set up within the crust of the Earth finally squeezed the droplets of crude oil from the muds and silts (*source rocks*) where they formed. Hydrocarbons making up crude oil are light, buoyant substances that rise easily through the water in overlying sediments. They may eventually seep out on to the Earth's surface and be lost. When an oilfield is formed, the crude oil is prevented from escaping by a layer of rock through which it cannot penetrate. Layers of shale, salt, gypsum and fine-grained limestones act in this way. The oil droplets then become 'trapped' by the so-called *cap-rock* and they can go on accumulating only in the more porous rocks underneath (reservoir rocks).

The presence of an oilfield may be indicated by seepage of a little of the crude oil on to the surface or by the escape of associated natural gas. In other cases, however, a full geological survey may be necessary. Geologists map the rocks in the area under investigation to discover what sort of structures have been developed and, if possible, what types of rock lie beneath the surface. Aerial photographs are often very useful in showing structures not obviously noticeable on the ground. The increasing demand for oil has led to the exploration of swamps, jungles and sea-floors where it is impossible to study the actual rocks themselves. Several techniques have consequently been developed to solve this problem. They all depend on the variation in properties of different rock types.

The seismic method involves creating an artificial earthquake with explosives. The speeds of the resulting shock waves are recorded at stations situated at different distances from the explosion. As the speeds depend upon the types of rocks through which the waves pass, knowledge of the

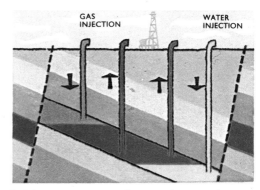

When the pressure of trapped gas and water in oil-bearing rock becomes low, oil is no longer driven from the sediment to the wells. An artificial pressure is made by driving gas and water into the oil-bearing rock.

99

underlying rocks and their depths is obtained. Some of the shock waves bounce off the surface between the different types of rock and are reflected back to the Earth's surface. This gives an alternative use for the seismic method; from the time taken for the reflected wave to complete its journey, the depth of the reflecting layer can be estimated and more information about the structure of the rocks obtained. With the *gravimetric* method, slight differences in the attraction due to gravity at the Earth's surface are measured. The differences depend on the densities of the type of rocks underneath. Finally, the *magnetic* method relates the intensity and direction of the Earth's magnetic field at a given point with the known magnetic properties of the different rock types. An estimation of what sorts of rock lie directly under the surface is then possible. Unfortunately there is as yet no method of accurately locating oilfields. The techniques of discovery used today can only inform the mining engineers of the whereabouts of the most likely places. Drilling alone proves whether oil is present or not.

CHAPTER TWENTY-TWO

Fuel from Ancient Forests

FALLEN leaves and branches on the forest floor are all fairly quickly acted upon by bacteria and broken down into simple chemical compounds that can be absorbed by other plants. This process of bacterial decomposition, however, requires plentiful supplies of oxygen. In waterlogged soil, only a small amount of decomposition occurs. Organic acids (e.g. humic acid) are formed and prevent bacterial action. The plant remains, both woody and non-woody, build up, layer upon layer, and a peat bog results.

Peat is a fibrous or woody material in which the plant remains are still fairly obvious. The cellulose and lignin walls of the plants are preserved. As the peat accumulates, the lower layers become compressed and lose some of their water. When dried, this compacted peat can be used as a low grade fuel. Prolonged burial (for millions of years) of such peat deposits has resulted in the formation of *coal*. The combined effect of pressure and heat gradually forced out the hydrogen and oxygen (in the form of water, carbon dioxide, methane, etc). This increased the percentage of carbon and the peat turned into coal. The most efficient heating coal is the one with the highest carbon content.

Rank of Coal

There are, in the Earth's crust, organic deposits of all stages, ranging from newly formed peat to the highest quality coal. The stage of alteration is the *rank* of the coal. Peat, which is not very different in composition from living plant material, has the lowest rank of all, and the lowest percentage of carbon. A little above peat in the

CARBONICOLA

A NON-MARINE MUSSEL

CALAMITES

A GIANT HORSETAIL STEM

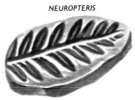

NEUROPTERIS

A FOSSIL SEED FERN

ANTHRACONAIA

A NON-MARINE MUSSEL

SOME COAL-MEASURE FOSSILS

A PRIMITIVE
COAL-FOREST
REPTILE

ranking is *lignite*. Plant structures can often be seen in it and show that it is derived mainly from forest peat (i.e. it is composed mainly of woody fragments).

Lignite is often called *brown coal*, especially when the plant structures are not clearly visible. These deposits are common in the Mesozoic and Tertiary rocks formed less than 200 million years ago. Brown coals are used locally as fuels but are not commercially important. There are very few brown-coal deposits in Britain but America and Australia are well endowed with them.

By far the most important coal is the *bituminous coal* originally laid down during the latter part of the Carboniferous period (Pennsylvanian) some 320 million years ago. Most of the world's supply of coal comes from these deposits (the *Coal Measures*). Bituminous coal is normally shiny and black and shows a banded structure. Plant remains are not visible to the naked eye. The highest ranked coal is *anthracite*, formed, it would appear, where the beds have been subjected to extreme pressure. It is a hard, brittle coal containing about 95% carbon and is a very efficient fuel. Its hot smokeless flame makes it suitable for many industrial and domestic uses.

As a rule the older the deposit, the higher the rank of coal. This is because the 'coalification' process has been going on for a longer period. However, in volcanic regions, where earth movements have created extra heat and/or pressure, bituminous coals have been found in Tertiary and Mesozoic deposits.

Bituminous Coal

Because of its importance, this type of coal has been studied more fully than any other. It contains between

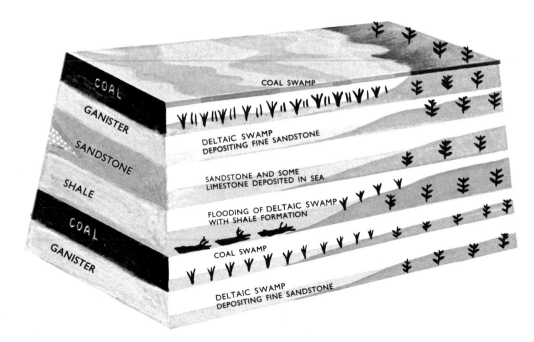

The rock sequences in the Coal Measures are the results of rhythmic sinking of the coastal swamps. Flooding of the swamps produced shales and marine deposits. Accumulation of these built up the sea-bed until swamps again developed.

70 and 90% of carbon, 8 to 15% oxygen and 4% hydrogen. There are also small amounts of sulphur and nitrogen – both of which are present in the material of living plants. All coals contain a certain amount of mineral matter derived partly from the original plants, but mainly from water percolating through the deposits during and after their formation. This mineral matter forms the ash when the coal is burnt.

Bituminous coal has a banded appearance and microscopic examination of the different layers shows that they are made up of different materials. The brightest bands are called *vitrain*. This material breaks easily into regularly-shaped pieces and is clean and shiny. It does not form extensive layers – only relatively small patches. Examination under the microscope shows that it is made up of altered wood and bark. Probably

each patch represents a single fallen tree. *Clarain* forms other bright bands, but these are layered themselves. There are very thin bands of vitrain, separated by a duller material called *durain*. Clarain is, in fact, a combination of vitrain and durain. The latter also forms bands alone. It is harder and duller than vitrain and is made up of spores (pollen) and many tiny fragments too small to be identified. The dirtiness of coal is due to a fourth material – *fusain*. It is a flaky charcoal-like material that occurs in thin layers in the coal seam. The coal splits along these layers quite easily and the fusain rubs off. How fusain is formed is not yet understood.

The Coal Measures

The earliest coal-bearing deposits of any value are of Carboniferous age (250 million years ago); presumably woody plants were not sufficiently advanced before this time, or

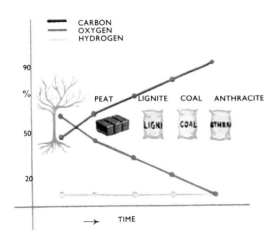

A graph showing how the percentages of carbon, oxygen and hydrogen change during coal formation.

conditions were not suitable for their widespread preservation. The main coal fields are situated in North West Europe, the U.S.S.R. and the Eastern part of North America. A study of the Carboniferous Coal Measures suggests that they were laid down in vast coastal swamps and that each seam represents the vegetation of a single swamp in position.

Actual coal forms only a small part (less than 5%) of the coal measures; shales, sandstones and mudstones together make up the bulk of the rocks. There is a clear sequence of rock types, repeated many times throughout the coal measures. Below each seam of coal there is a bed of fine sandstone (*ganister*) in which there are often impressions and casts of plant roots. This is further evidence that the coal seams are formed *in situ* on the site of the old swamp. Above this ganister is the coal itself. Clarain and vitrain represent the accumulation of normal plant material while durain, containing only assorted small frag-

ments, probably represents the accumulation of material during temporary flooding. Occasional strips of sand would represent washout streams, flowing through the swamp. Plant remains within the coal indicate that the principal inhabitants of the forest swamps were giant club-mosses such as *Lepidodendron* and *Sigillaria*, and huge horsetails (*Calamites*). Smaller fern-like plants existed beneath them. Insects such as dragonflies were common but no birds or flowering plants were to be found. It has been estimated that twenty feet of plant debris went into every foot of coal seam. Coal seams vary from a few millimetres to fifty feet or more. The larger ones represent vast accumulations of plant debris.

Above the coal seams there are normally shales – muddy and sandy deposits. They contain many shells of freshwater mussels and remains of fern-like plants such as *Neuropteris*. These freshwater deposits indicate a sinking of the swamps and the accumulation of still or slowly moving water. Many of the shales are followed by marine deposits – limestones and sandstones, indicating complete sinking of the coastal swamps. There must also have been uplift of the inland regions for much sediment was deposited around the coasts and eventually built up to sea-level again. Swamp conditions again prevailed and the next coal seam was formed.

To accommodate the vast thicknesses of the coal measures there must have been a great deal of subsidence of this type but this is consistent with the other earth movements that were going on at the time. They culminated in the *Hercynian* or *Armorican* earth movements which brought the Carboniferous Period to a close.

CHAPTER TWENTY-THREE

Natural Gas

ONE of the major hazards facing the coal-miner is *fire-damp*. This is a colourless, odourless gas that escapes from the coal seams. It can be ignited by the smallest spark and such explosions have caused many pit-disasters. The same gas often bubbles to the surface when the mud of a stagnant pond or swamp is disturbed. For this reason, it is often called *marsh gas*. Under the name *natural gas*, it occurs in large quantities in association with oil deposits.

Natural gas is not a simple compound but a mixture of a number of gases. The commonest of these is *methane* – CH_4 which may be present as 50–90% of the gas. The other substances in natural gas are mainly *ethane*, *propane* and *butane* – higher members of the same series as methane (the paraffin series).

Natural gas is formed when dead organisms decay in the absence of free oxygen. Bacterial action slowly removes the oxygen bound up in the material and leaves carbon and hydrogen (the other two main elements in living organisms). These combine to form various *hydrocarbons* such as methane. As the sediments become buried, pressure and heat continue to force out the gaseous materials. The process is slow, however, and coal that

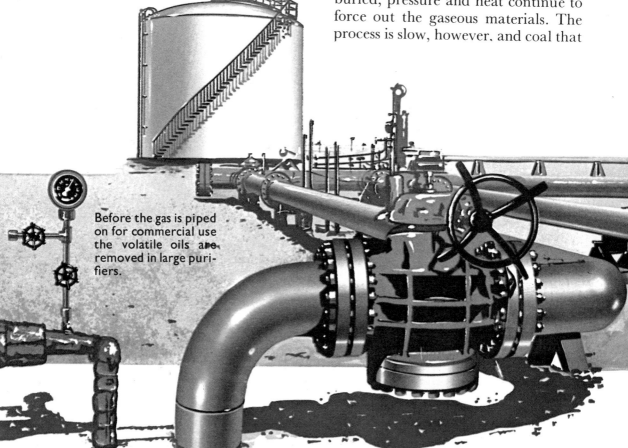

Before the gas is piped on for commercial use the volatile oils are removed in large purifiers.

has been buried for millions of years still contains a fair amount of gaseous and volatile material. This accounts for the presence of methane in mines and is the basis of the coal-gas industry. When strongly heated without air, coal gives off *coal-gas* (mainly hydrogen and methane) together with tar and other oily materials. The residue (coke) is almost pure carbon.

The huge reservoirs of natural gas associated with petroleum deposits reflect the different origins of coal and oil. Coal was formed in swamps from woody plant-remains, whereas oil is believed to be derived from the bodies of countless millions of marine organisms (plankton). Presumably these plants and animals sank in partly land-locked seas where oxygen was short, and began to decay. Planktonic organisms contain far more fats and oils than woody plants. Fats contain a higher proportion of hydrogen than other carbohydrate materials. This means that more hydrogen is available to form hydrocarbons. Not only the gaseous forms, such as methane, but the many compounds that make up crude petroleum must have been formed in this sort of way. Bubbles of gas and oil became trapped in the sediment and gradually covered. The pressure of overlying rocks forced the oil and gas into porous rocks such as sandstone where they are now found, effectively sealed by cappings of clay or other impervious rock.

Until fairly recently, natural gas was allowed to escape from many oil-wells as a waste material. It is, however, the most efficient of all fuel gases (containing more than 95% combustible hydrocarbons) and every effort is now made to conserve the supplies and make efficient use of them. Gas is often used as a source of power at the oil

In the never-ending search for oil and gas, drilling-rigs such as this are being erected in likely places all over the world.

wells themselves and can easily be transported by pipeline for use elsewhere. For some time natural gas has been the main fuel gas in parts of the U.S.A., and many other countries are following their example. Huge tankers have been constructed to carry liquid methane (natural gas) from the Algerian Sahara to Great Britain. Even allowing for the cost of transport, the gas is cheaper than coal gas because of its superior heating efficiency. Hence the tremendous economic interest shown by consumers and industrialists in the natural gas developments in the North Sea.

Where a piped gas supply is not available, 'bottled' gas is often used. This is mainly butane and propane which are easily liquefied by cooling or compression of natural gas, and 'bottled' under pressure.

Some sewage purification works produce a great deal of methane in the sludge digesters. The gas is used to power the equipment at the works and has also been used to drive lorries. In terms of saving on other fuels, the methane is a very valuable by-product.

CHAPTER TWENTY-FOUR

Heat from the Earth

NEEDING more and more energy to drive the world's machinery, Man constantly seeks new sources of power. Apart from burning coal and oil, he now breaks down the atoms of radio-active elements (*atomic energy*), dams the rivers (*hydraulic energy*) and directly converts the Sun's heat (*solar energy*). Even the force of the winds and the great tidal movements of the seas have been harnessed. One further source of energy, likely to be of the very greatest importance in the future, is the heat generated in the Earth itself – *geothermal heat*.

What causes the Earth's heat is not absolutely certain but there can be no doubting its existence. In numerous parts of the world great quantities of molten lava are thrown out of volcanoes, steam escapes through natural vents, mud pools boil, and scalding water is brought to the surface as hot springs or geysers. The estimated amount of energy locked away in the

Earth vastly exceeds that contained in conventional fuels. All that is required is to turn it into a form which can be used by Man – *geothermal power*.

The benefits of the Earth's heat are not entirely a modern discovery. Icelanders have long piped water from hot springs into their homes and horticultural greenhouses. Today the domestic dwellings of 46,000 people (one quarter of Iceland's population) are geothermally heated. At Larderello, near Pisa in Northern Italy, hot gases escaping at the surface have been used to generate electricity since the beginning of this century.

But until very recently, geothermal power was thought of as a very unimportant source of energy – a mere make-weight to the other great natural supplies. Then, at a United Nations conference held at Rome in 1961, the whole subject was discussed by a gathering of chemists, geologists and

Geysers are hot springs which discharge boiling water and steam only at intervals. Beneath the ground is a system of intercommunicating chambers which fill up with hot water. At the bottom, water becomes super-heated – its temperature is more than 100°C; but owing to the weight of water above, it cannot boil. Slowly the temperature of the water near the surface rises. Finally some of it boils off as steam. The pressure is sufficiently lowered for the super-heated water below to also boil and the violent surge of steam that follows may throw water hundreds of feet in the air.

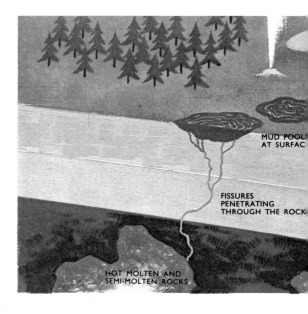

MUD POOL AT SURFAC

FISSURES PENETRATING THROUGH THE ROCK

HOT MOLTEN AND SEMI-MOLTEN ROCKS

engineers. Further information had become available from a geothermal project at Wairakei, New Zealand and elsewhere. The conclusion reached was that geothermal power was capable of providing large quantities of electricity in many parts of the world.

New Zealand's Wairakei Project

In the centre of North Island, New Zealand, a triangular section of land 150 miles long and 30 miles wide, exhibits at its surface every known natural phenomenon associated with heat from the Earth. These include hot springs, numerous steam vents and one active volcano.

Hot water had previously been used in the area for domestic heating. But in 1950 a scheme was put under way tapping supplies of underground steam to generate electricity. By 1958 the power station on the Waikato river was providing New Zealand with her first geothermal electricity.

The underground steam is brought up through bore-holes from depths of between 500 and 3000 feet. Steam from 500 feet was found capable of exerting a pressure of 70 pounds per square inch in excess of atmospheric pressure; from over 2000 feet the pressure exerted is more than 200 pounds per square inch.

Unlike the 'dry' steam of Larderello in Italy, the New Zealand steam is generally 'wet'. It comes to the surface mixed between four and six times its own volume of water. Each borehead is therefore equipped with a piece of apparatus which separates hot water from the steam. The steam is transmitted more than a mile from the chief boring area to the power station sited on the Waikato river. The hot water which is also at a high pressure, is run into the so-called 'silencers'. Here the pressure is lowered, and the water boils, 'flashing off' large quantities of steam. One day this steam will also be used.

In the power station the pressure of geothermal steam drives the turbines causing electricity to be generated. Once used, the steam is condensed in water taken from the river. The condensation creates a vacuum and this sucks more steam through the turbines. The steam from the Earth is not, however, completely pure. It contains quantities of the gases carbon dioxide

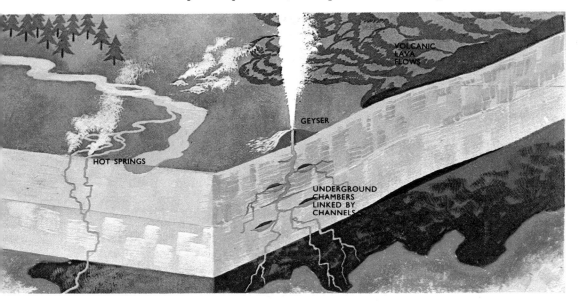

Readings taken in mine shafts and bore-holes show that temperatures in the outer regions of the Earth's crust steadily increase with depth – on the average about 1°C every 100 feet.

The heat is thought to be mainly produced by natural breakdown of radio-active elements (the same process by which energy is produced in atomic power stations). Some heat may also be generated by chemical changes under intense pressure or by friction between moving rocks.

The temperature at the bottom of the crust has been estimated at 600–750°C – not sufficiently high to melt the rock there. There is no evidence either of a fluid layer in the outer regions of the Earth. The *magma* (molten rock) that does form is believed to be due to local concentra-tion of heat by some process not as yet fully understood.

Hot springs and geysers develop where super-heated steam and gas rises from subterranean sources and heats up water circulating at higher levels. Alternatively the circulating water may itself penetrate to very deep levels and come in contact with hot rock.

Most hot water coming to the surface is *meteoric* water – that is normal rain-water which has seeped into the Earth. Some is probably derived from ancient buried sediments while a little is thought to be reaching the surface for the first time (*juvenile water*). The steam used to generate electricity is tapped from 'steam-fields' – supplies of superheated steam sealed up inside the Earth.

and hydrogen sulphide. Not being very soluble in water, these gases accumulate and have to be pumped out with air pumps. Otherwise the vacuum would be destroyed.

Advantages of Geothermal Power

Perhaps the greatest advantage of electricity from geothermal sources is its cheapness. Some expenditure is needed for preliminary surveying, for drilling for steam and for fitting transmission pipes. Considerably more is then required for installing the generating plant. But thereafter only maintenance costs have to be thought of. There are no heavy fuel bills and such processes as purification and combustion of fuels are avoided.

This economic aspect is especially important for undeveloped countries. They desperately need power for their new factories and irrigation schemes but have not the money to instal and run atomic energy plants or build the huge dams necessary for hydroelectric power.

A second advantage of geothermal electricity is that the supply is constant. There is no dependence upon fuel supply nor even upon the seasonal fluctuation of rainfall which limits hydraulic power. Yet geothermal power is very easily controlled. If more electricity is being generated than meets the demand it is a simple matter to shut off the supply of steam with suitable valves.

A third advantage is that some of the most likely areas for developing geo-thermal electricity are in just those parts handicapped by having no natural fuels. Apart from New Zealand, Iceland and Italy, localities in California, Japan, Kenya, Mexico, Salvador, Java, Argentina, Chile, Algeria, Bolivia and Colombia all have geysers, hot springs, volcanoes and so on, displayed at the surface.

It will be noticed that most of these places are located on the Earth's great belts of crustal weakness – regions where earthquakes occur. One belt rings the Pacific – from Tierra del

Fuego, along the Western coasts of North and South America, and then down the East coast of Asia to New Zealand. The second belt runs from Afghanistan westward to Southern Europe and North Africa. The third follows the unstable rift valley belt from the Dead Sea in Jordan through Abyssinia and Kenya to Tanzania.

But just as some of the richest oil-fields give no indication of their presence at the Earth's surface, it is probable that hot gases are not all located in unstable volcanic regions. Further exploration may reveal supplies of hot gases in all parts of the world.

Drilling for Hot Gas

Drilling in 'hot ground' is a skilled and dangerous task. Care is needed to ensure that any steam or hot water located does not rush to the surface and wreck the drilling equipment or endanger the lives of the engineers.

Consequently liquid mud is forced down the bore at very high pressures all the time drilling is in progress. Near the surface of the ground a large mushroom-shaped cavity is excavated. Any sudden upsurge of hot water that does take place can expand safely into the cavity while safety precautions are taken.

From the borings that have been carried out, there seems to be considerable variation in the properties of the steam. Its qualities change according to both depth and locality. These variables are of temperature, pressure, contamination (other gases, salt, silica) and comparative 'wetness' and 'dryness'. All are important in assessing the economic value of the 'strike', as is the distance of the bore from a populated centre or a power station.

The best bores are found to be where a cavern or crack is penetrated. Here

MUDPOOL

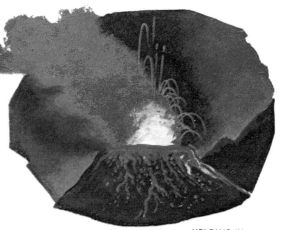

VOLCANO IN ERUPTION

HOT SPRINGS

The Earth's heat is displayed at the surface in some parts of the world. (Above) *A boiling mud-pool* (middle) *An erupting volcano* (bottom) *Hot springs.*

A trial borehole in New Zealand. The bore has been sunk in 'hot' ground releasing steam trapped beneath the surface. The steam is allowed to escape for a trial period before it is economically used.

Left, apparatus (silencers) at bore-heads lowers the pressure of hot water and 'flashes' if off as surplus steam.

Right, at Wairakei, steam is pumped more than a mile from the bore area to the power station on the banks of the Waikato river.

hot water in the surrounding rock can easily flow as steam into the open space. Other bores yielding a good supply of steam are in heavily fissured rock; the fissures enable fluid to move from all directions to the bottom of the bore.

Before full exploitation of a bore is made, it must be made certain that the supply located will yield sufficient steam over a large period. Usually a very small bore is made and then left to 'blow' for a couple of years. Regular and hot water will continue to flow. Perhaps in some regions the flow will be continuous with super-heated water escaping from the depths being replaced by cold *meteoric* water percolating downwards from the surface of the Earth. Certainly the expected life of a steam 'field' must be estimated in tens of years if not in larger units of time. The Larderello steam which now generates two-thirds of the electricity needed for Italy's railways has been flowing without any apparent slacken-

Inspecting a bore-head at Wairakei, New Zealand. The steam from this bore is brought up from 1,800 feet.

inspection of the quality and quantity of the steam together with its pressure and temperature is carried out before any decision is made.

Not enough information is at present available on just how long the steam ing for more than half a century. Another promising indication is that most of the hot spring and boiling mud pools seem to have occupied the same sites for many centuries.

CHAPTER TWENTY-FIVE

Where Metals come from

PURE metals are rarely found in the Earth's crust. Nearly always they are combined with other elements forming metallic compounds. Iron, for instance, may combine with oxygen or sulphur to form oxides or sulphides.

The quantity of metals in the crust is relatively small. If they were scattered at random, there would never be sufficient concentration of

LAYERED IGNEOUS ROCK – EACH BAND IS COMPOSED OF A DIFFERENT MINERAL. THE BUSHVELD INTRUSION OF SOUTH AFRICA PROVIDES GOOD EXAMPLES OF SUCH ROCKS. IT SUPPLIES MUCH OF THE WORLD'S CHROMIUM AND PLATINUM

Crystals cool at different temperatures. Early crystals of high density sink to the bottom of intrusions; crystals of lower density rise while segregations may occur throughout.

one kind to make extraction worthwhile. Enormous quantities of rock would have to be treated to get a very small quantity of metal.

Fortunately there have been a number of geologic processes during the past history of the Earth which

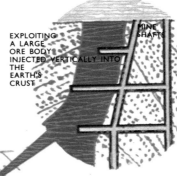

EXPLOITING A LARGE ORE BODY INJECTED VERTICALLY INTO THE EARTH'S CRUST

MINE SHAFTS

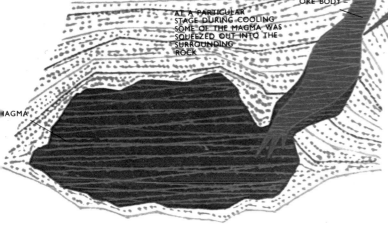

AT A PARTICULAR STAGE DURING COOLING SOME OF THE MAGMA WAS SQUEEZED OUT INTO THE SURROUNDING ROCK

ORE BODY

MAGMA

During crystallization intense pressure may squeeze part of a differentiated magma into surrounding rocks. This part may be particularly rich in some metals. An example is the Sudbury intrusion of Canada which supplies the world with most of its nickel.

have concentrated the metallic compounds. When a rock contains enough to make extraction worthwhile it is called an *ore*.

There are three kinds of rock, *igneous* (cooled from a molten state), *sedimentary* (built up of weathered fragments of earlier rock) and *metamorphic* (rock altered by temperatures and pressures). All three may be ore-bearing, though the methods by which the metal becomes concentrated vary.

The concentration of metal necessary for a rock to become an ore depends very much upon exactly what metal it is. Copper-bearing rock, for instance, becomes an ore if only 0·7% of its volume is made up of copper, but such a low percentage is not an economic proposition for aluminium: the concentration of this metal must be at least about 30%. Such figures largely depend upon the comparative rarities of the metals but also upon commercial demands.

Igneous and Metamorphic Ores

Igneous rocks have cooled from *magma* – that is rock in a molten state. During the process, some minerals solidify before others. In the semi-fluid surroundings, these minerals may sink and become separated as a layer quite early in the proceedings. The mineral may be rich in a particular metal. For instance the mineral chromite contains chromium.

Later formed, metal-bearing minerals may crystallize in the spaces between older minerals, forming valuable segregations for the prospector and miner. The last of the magma to solidify (*residual magma*) may have become enriched in titanium, iron or other metals and on solidifying forms worthwhile deposits.

The most valuable of the magmatic deposits are connected with great injections of *basic* magma into the crust. Basic magma has, in its original state, only a small quantity of silica and has a larger proportion of certain metals – iron, titanium, chromium.

Acidic magmas which cool to form granites and related rocks are rich in silica. The quantity of metals they contain is correspondingly small. Yet granitic masses are associated with many of the rarer metallic elements – uranium, copper, cobalt, manganese, zinc, tin, lead, silver, gold. Such ores

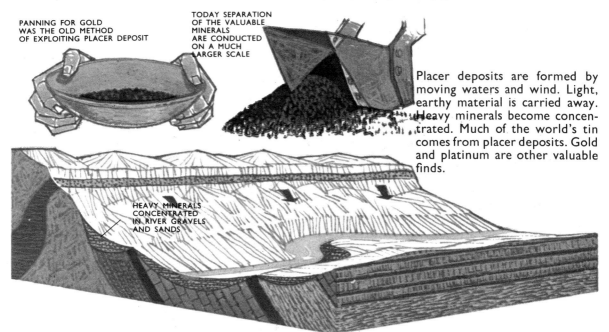

PANNING FOR GOLD WAS THE OLD METHOD OF EXPLOITING PLACER DEPOSIT

TODAY SEPARATION OF THE VALUABLE MINERALS ARE CONDUCTED ON A MUCH LARGER SCALE

Placer deposits are formed by moving waters and wind. Light, earthy material is carried away. Heavy minerals become concentrated. Much of the world's tin comes from placer deposits. Gold and platinum are other valuable finds.

HEAVY MINERALS CONCENTRATED IN RIVER GRAVELS AND SANDS

do not occur within the granites. They occur in the surrounding or *country* rock. What happens is that when most of the acidic magma has cooled hot volatile gases and water at very high temperatures emanate from the cooling mass into the surrounding rock. Sulphur, fluorine, boron, chlorine, and phosphorus were contained in solution, and so also were a variety of rare metals.

Probably a lot of the metals were originally present in sediments deposited by the sea. When the hot magma became intruded, much of the sediment including the traces of metals became incorporated into the magma. The metals were unable to pass into the crystals of earlier formed minerals as their atoms were too large. Consequently they became concentrated in the hot residual solutions. When the solutions passed out into the surrounding rocks, metallic salts solidified along cracks and gulleys to form valuable mineral veins.

Passing away from the granitic intrusion, the belts of mineral veins often alter. For instance, in Cornwall,

tin veins pass outwards into copper veins. Then follow veins of lead, silver, antimony and finally iron and manganese. This zonal arrangement is largely due to the different solubilities of minerals. As the fluid passes outwards, so its temperature and pressure become lower. Minerals are precipitated in reverse order of their solubilities.

Metamorphism is a process in which both igneous and sedimentary rocks are subjected to increased temperatures and pressures. Hot solutions may again selectively dissolve and attack the less resistant minerals and redeposit concentrated metal compounds as ore bodies.

Sedimentary Ores

The process of weathering at the Earth's surface continually breaks down older rocks. The fragments, either as solid particles or in solution, are usually transported and deposited elsewhere to form new rocks. The deposition of metal-bearing minerals requires a suitable source of supply and favourable conditions for precipitation. Sometimes the action of living

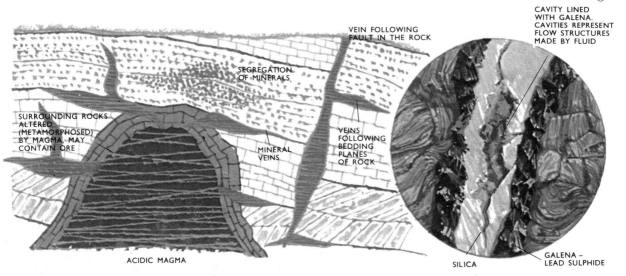

Volatile fluids move from a cooled acid magma out into surrounding rocks. The fluids follow paths of weakness-bedding planes and faults. The metals associated with such magmas make up some of the world's most important ores.

organisms such as bacteria is involved. Particularly important sedimentary ores are the ironstones – iron carbonates and silicates.

Some minerals weathered from rocks are highly resistant to decomposition. In addition they may have a high density. Water movement may remove lighter material and leave behind a concentration of mineral. Such deposits are called placer deposits. Gold, platinum and tin, iron and titanium minerals may occur in this way.

Alternatively the process of weathering may remove some substances from a rock or soil and leave behind a deposit richer in a certain mineral. Bauxite – the ore of aluminium – is left behind after certain soils are weathered in hot climates.

Uranium minerals are radioactive and can be detected with geiger counters. Layers of soil shield the radiation so geigers are lowered into specially prepared pits or bore-holes. Alternatively, cores of rock from bore holes are investigated.

Mineral Prospecting

The most promising regions for mineral prospecting are those areas which have been subjected to igneous and metamorphic activity. Here are the best chances of finding rich mineral veins. A geological survey begins usually with a rapid reconnaisance often using aerial photographs followed by more detailed work. Mapping the surface rocks reveals something of the geological history of the area – the various episodes of igneous and metamorphic activity that have taken place.

Geological mapping and inspection of mineral veins at the surface gives a good framework for exploration. The most likely places for ore are often pin-pointed. Today, further assistance is provided by geochemists and geophysicists and a complete survey of an area combines many techniques.

Geochemical prospecting consists of analysing numerous samples of soil, rock, water sediment, even plants. Concentrations of metals can be estimated in quantities as small as a few parts per billion. Appreciable increases of metal in soils and so on may indicate a possible rich ore somewhere in the vicinity.

Geophysicists use a wide range of instruments. The magnetometer is sensitive to the variations of the magnetic field of the Earth. A greater intensity of magnetic field occurs over magnetic mineral concentrations. Magnetometers can be flown over areas by aircraft and are particularly valuable over seas and lakes or in inaccessible regions, e.g. mountainous country. A number of electrical methods of exploration are used. For instance the resistivity of the rocks to an electric current can be measured. Non-metalliferous rocks are not good conductors and have a high resistivity whereas metalliferous rocks are much better conductors and have low resistivity.

The gravimetric method depends upon the great gravitational attraction of dense metal-containing bodies while the seismic method locates possible ore bodies by the character of shock waves through the Earth.

CHAPTER TWENTY-SIX

Identifying Minerals

ALL minerals have a definite chemical composition (i.e., they represent a certain combination of elements) and definite physical characteristics (in relation to hardness, lustre, transparency, etc.) by which they may be recognised. The vast

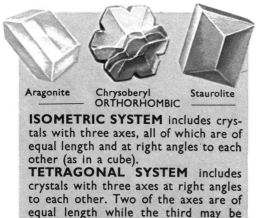

Aragonite   Chrysoberyl   Staurolite
ORTHORHOMBIC

ISOMETRIC SYSTEM includes crystals with three axes, all of which are of equal length and at right angles to each other (as in a cube).
TETRAGONAL SYSTEM includes crystals with three axes at right angles to each other. Two of the axes are of equal length while the third may be either longer or shorter.
ORTHORHOMBIC SYSTEM includes crystals with three axes at right angles to each other but all of different lengths.
TRICLINIC SYSTEM includes crystals with three axes, all of different lengths and none of which forms a right angle with another.
HEXAGONAL SYSTEM includes crystals with four axes. Three of these axes are of equal length and horizontal. The angles between them are also equal. The fourth axis is at right angles to the other three (i.e., vertical) and may be longer or shorter than them.
MONOCLINIC SYSTEM includes crystals with three axes, all of different lengths and only two of which form a right angle.

Albite   Rhodonite   Axinite
TRICLINIC

majority of minerals have a definite crystal structure. In other words the smallest particles in the mineral are arranged as a regular, repeating pattern like the tiles in a mosaic. A few minerals, however, are non-crystalline, i.e., they have no definite shape, like opal (a form of quartz), and are called *amorphous*. Some minerals are fairly easy to identify but others resemble each other so closely that a number of tests are needed to distinguish between them.

Crystallography

There are six great systems of crystal forms: *isometric*, *tetragonal*, *hexagonal*, *orthorhombic*, *monoclinic*, and *triclinic*. The division is based upon imaginary lines or *axes* passing through the centre of a crystal—their number, relative lengths and relative angles. In the isometric system, for instance, the crystals have three axes, each of equal length and each at right angles to each other (as, for instance, in a cube).

Common rock salt, or halite, is composed of lots of little cubes (though such an arrangement of the axes can produce far more shapes than just a cube). The size of crystals varies tremendously; some are too

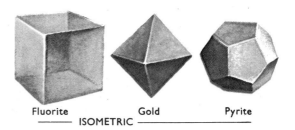

Fluorite   Gold   Pyrite
ISOMETRIC

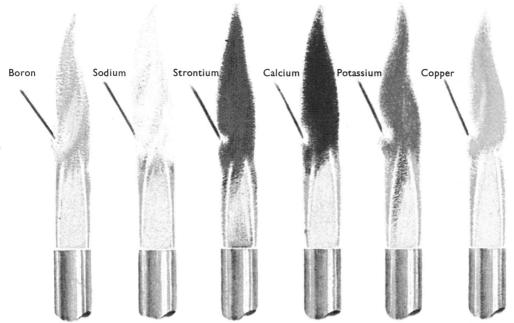

Boron   Sodium   Strontium   Calcium   Potassium   Copper

Chemical Tests

A great number of chemical tests can be used to diagnose the nature of an unknown mineral. The *flame* test relies upon the fact that a mineral will colour a flame according to the metal it contains. The sodium minerals (albite, glauberite, halite, borax, chabazite, lazurite, oligoclase, etc.) will colour a flame strong yellow. The strontium minerals (strontianite and celestite) will give it a glorious crimson-red colour (strontium goes into many fireworks). The copper minerals (azurite, bornite, chalcopyrite, malachite, tetrahedrite, etc.) colour a flame either blue or green, and so on. The blowpipe test involves heating the mineral in a powdered form on a charcoal block. Heating anglesite, for instance, in this way produces a ball of lead.

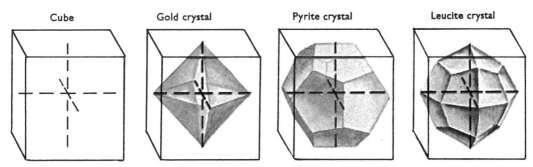

Cube   Gold crystal   Pyrite crystal   Leucite crystal

Some of the minerals listed in the same system may, at first glance, seem to be quite different. But the important thing is that their axes have certain similar characteristics with regard to number, length and relative angles. Every crystal in the isometric system, for example, could be cut from a cube without altering its axes.

Apatite   Zincite   Zircon   Scapolite   Realgar   Augite
—— HEXAGONAL ——   —— TETRAGONAL ——   —— MONOCLINIC ——

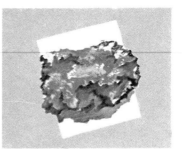

Some minerals are quite transparent and print may be read through them with ease. Others are opaque and others still somewhere in between.

small to be studied by the naked eye while crystals of spodumene have been found close on fifty feet in length. The trouble with examining crystals is that perfect specimens are very rarely found and it takes a lot of experience to be able to reconstruct the whole crystal from a mere fragment.

Specific Gravity

A good lead towards the identity of an unknown mineral is its *specific gravity*, i.e., the weight of a piece of the mineral compared with the weight of an equal volume of water. Sulphur has a specific gravity of 2, corundum 4, cassiterite 7 and so on. It needs a special apparatus to find the specific gravity so this cannot be done in the field but it is possible to distinguish between lighter and heavier minerals (provided both lumps are the same size) simply by comparing them in your hands. A piece of talc (specific gravity 2·8) seems considerably lighter than a piece of apatite (specific gravity 3·2).

Mohs' Scale of Hardness

An easier characteristic of minerals to determine is hardness. This can be done by means of the *scratch test* which is based upon the simple fact that a harder mineral scratches a softer one. There is a scale of hardness, called

Galena may be scratched by calcite (hardness 3 on Mohs' scale) but will itself scratch gypsum (hardness 2), so its hardness must be about 2.5 on this scale.

Mohs' Scale after the Austrian mineralogist who devised it as a possible means of identifying minerals. It uses ten minerals, each a little harder than the one before, namely: 1 talc (the softest), 2 gypsum, 3 calcite, 4 fluorspar, 5 apatite, 6 orthoclase, 7 quartz, 8 topaz, 9 corundum, 10 diamond. In order to find the hardness of any mineral you simply find the *softest* mineral in the set that will scratch it. Galena, for instance, will be scratched by calcite but will itself scratch gypsum, so its hardness is about 2·5. Iron pyrites (Fool's gold), has a hardness on Mohs' scale of 6 to 6·5. This quickly distinguishes it from real gold which has a hardness of only 2·5 to 3. You can buy a hardness set of minerals. Number 10, the diamond, is usually left out because of the cost but it does not really matter because you are not likely to find a mineral harder than corundum (if you did it would be a diamond).

The hardness of a mineral can be roughly determined without the aid of a hardness set. A fingernail has a hardness on Mohs' scale of about 2·5, a piece of glass about 5·5 and the blade of a knife about 6·5.

Minerals and Light

Some minerals are *transparent*, i.e., you can see through them clearly. Other minerals are *opaque*, i.e., no light is transmitted through them at all. Then there are the minerals in between, which let through a certain amount of light only. But many minerals classed as opaque will let a certain amount of light through if they are ground down to a very fine film.

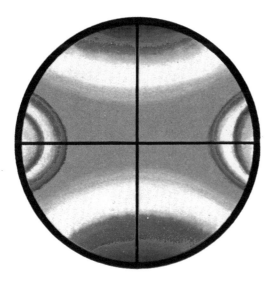

When viewed through a polarizing microscope a wonderful pattern of colours may be seen in this thin section of muscovite (one of the mica minerals).

Other Means of Identification

Electricity and Magnetism

Another guide is the electrical and magnetic characteristics of minerals. Metallic minerals are good conductors of electricity whereas the non-metallic minerals, generally, are not. All mineral crystals develop an electric charge when rubbed but it can be seen more clearly in some than others. The only mineral that is strikingly attracted to a magnet is magnetite, though others, such as platinum, pyrrhotite, ilmenite, haematite and chromite show a half-hearted response when placed next to a magnet. Lodestone, a rare form of magnetite, is a natural magnet.

Radioactivity

One thing that has greatly helped the search for uranium is the fact that all uranium minerals (there are over 100, though only a few are important) are radioactive, i.e., they emit radiations which can be detected by a Geiger counter. The radiations cause electrical disturbances which produce 'clicks' in a loudspeaker. The same applies to the thorium minerals.

Minerals and Heat

The characteristics of minerals with regard to heat are important. The electrical resistance of conducting minerals, (the amount of difficulty electrons have in flowing through a substance), for instance, increases with increased temperature. Different minerals fuse (melt) at different temperatures. Stibnite will fuse in a candle flame (about 500°C) while a thin splinter of orthoclase will just about fuse in a blow-lamp flame (about 1,300°C).

When a real diamond and a paste diamond are placed in a liquid which bends light rays entering it by the same amount as the paste diamond, only the real diamond will remain visible.

Some minerals take on new colours when exposed to ultra-violet light and are said to fluoresce. Some specimens of fluorite fluoresce with a strange bluish colour.

Colour is an important characteristic of minerals and an important clue in identification, especially where metallic minerals are concerned, for their colours are usually constant, with only slight variations in shade. But in minerals like quartz, corundum and garnet colour is often due to impurities and may vary considerably. And with some minerals, e.g., tourmaline, you can look at them behind the light and they will have one colour (or maybe more) but look at them in front of the light and the colour changes.

The *streak* of a mineral is its colour when it has been ground to a powder. It may differ from the superficial colour of the mineral but the great advantage is that the streak varies little from specimen to specimen whereas the superficial colour may. The superficial colour of talc, for instance, is green but its streak is white. Similarly, haematite, with a superficial colour of grey or black has a streak of reddish-brown.

The *lustre* of a mineral (its 'shine') depends upon the amount of light it absorbs or reflects. It may be described as resinous (like beeswax or resin) (e.g., sulphur), pearly (e.g., mica), silky (satin-like sheen) (e.g., chrysotile), vitreous (glassy) (e.g., quartz), adamantine (flashing) (e.g.,

diamond) or metallic (e.g., all of the metallic minerals). Minerals without any lustre are said to be *dull* (e.g., kaolinite).

An interesting optical characteristic of minerals is the degree to which they bend light rays. Light rays always change direction when passing from one medium to another (this is why a stick in water appears to be bent) and the greater the difference in optical density between the two the greater the amount of bending (water is denser than air, for instance). Every mineral has its own refractive index (the amount it bends light rays). This is one sure way of distinguishing between real and fake gems.

Some minerals, when exposed to ultra-violet light, show wonderful colours which previously they did not appear to have. These minerals are said to *fluoresce*. They include, among others, the uranium minerals. Some minerals fluoresce through impurities. Others fluoresce if they come from one locality but not if they come from another, or fluoresce with different colours from different localities. One of the most beautiful fluorescent minerals is the ruby (a variety of corundum) which emits a brilliant red glow when subjected to ultra-violet light.

The special optical characteristics

of a mineral when ground down to a
fine film and viewed through a
polarizing microscope may be a guide
to identification. It is also a fascinating study in its own right. Polarized
light is a special form of light which,
when passed through a thin section
of the mineral may produce a wonderful pattern of colours.

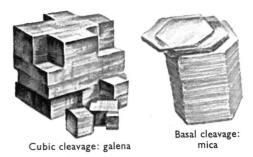

Cubic cleavage: galena

Basal cleavage:
mica

Cleavage and Fracture

The way in which a mineral breaks
is another clue to its identity. *Cleavage* is the way in which some minerals
tend to split along certain flat planes.
Cleavage can be revealed by breaking
a crystal of the mineral and noting
how it splits. The type of cleavage
is described by the number of cleavage planes and their relative angles.
To take a simple example, galena
has a *cubic* cleavage; there are three
cleavage planes at right angles to each
other. So, if you smash a cubic
galena crystal it will tend to break up
into a number of smaller, shiny cubes.
One of the most interesting types is
basal cleavage where there is just one
cleavage plane, parallel to the base of
the crystal. The best example of this
is to be found in the mica minerals,
which can be split into extremely
thin sheets.

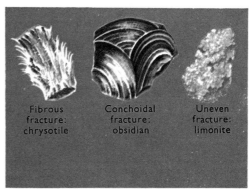

Fibrous
fracture:
chrysotile

Conchoidal
fracture:
obsidian

Uneven
fracture:
limonite

A mineral which does not break
along a cleavage plane is said to
fracture. All minerals *can* fracture but
are not likely to do so if they have a
good cleavage. There are a number
of different types of fracture, e.g.,
even, uneven, fibrous, conchoidal
(shell-like) etc. Chrysotile (the major
source of asbestos) has such a fibrous
fracture that the strands can be spun
and woven. Conchoidal fracture is
best seen in the rock obsidian (volcanic glass).

CHAPTER TWENTY-SEVEN

Commercially Important Minerals

THE commercial value of a mineral
generally depends upon its useful-
ness or decorative qualities and its
availability.

Since silicon and oxygen are by far
the most abundant elements in the
Earth's crust it is not surprising that
silica or quartz, which is a combin-

ation of the two, is the most common
mineral. But though quartz is literally
as common as sand (most grains of
sand *are* quartz) not all forms of this
mineral are valueless. Pure water-clear
quartz, known as rock crystal, is cut
into beads and ornaments and has
varied uses in the optical and elect-

rical industries. When it contains certain impurities it is even more valuable. A trace of manganese imparts a beautiful violet tint, giving amethyst; or the presence of iron produces citrine and cairngorm. Other forms of quartz classed as semiprecious stones include agate, sard, onyx, jasper, and opal.

Probably the most famed gemstone of all is the diamond. This is simply pure carbon. The popularity of the diamond is due to its hardness (it is the hardest of all minerals), brilliance and the way it strongly disperses light (this gives it 'fire'). It may be colourless or tinted with yellow, blue, pink, etc. For hundreds of years India was the only source of these valuable stones but today the leading producer of high quality diamonds is the Republic of South Africa. The high price commanded by diamonds, and by all other gems for that matter, lies in their rarity, though it is an interesting fact that such large diamond deposits have been found in recent years that their sale has been restricted in order to maintain their market value.

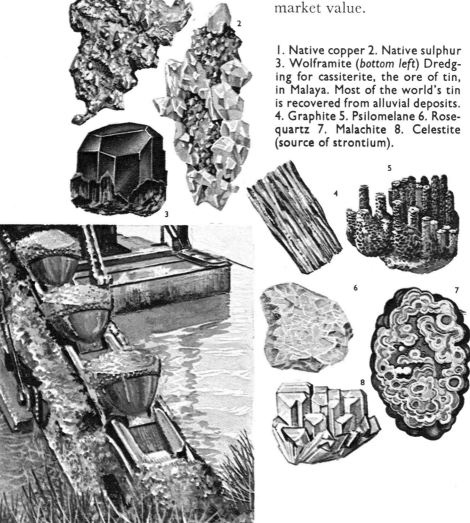

1. Native copper 2. Native sulphur 3. Wolframite (*bottom left*) Dredging for cassiterite, the ore of tin, in Malaya. Most of the world's tin is recovered from alluvial deposits. 4. Graphite 5. Psilomelane 6. Rosequartz 7. Malachite 8. Celestite (source of strontium).

Due to their exceptional hardness diamonds also have a great industrial value, mainly for drilling, cutting and smoothing.

Strangely enough, it is not the diamond which commands the highest price but the deep red 'pigeon's blood' ruby. Rubies, like sapphires, are gem forms of corundum (aluminium oxide), the only difference between them being in colour. The term sapphire includes all other colours of gem corundum, though the traditional colour is blue. Emerald is a form of beryl (a silicate of beryllium and aluminium).

The metallic minerals are of far more real value than any gemstone. The progress of civilisation is in fact reflected in man's increasing knowledge of metals and the minerals from which they are derived.

The metal which has probably played the most useful role in history in one form or another is iron. Chunks of pure iron do not occur in the earth and the most important ore of this metal is haematite (an oxide of iron). Haematite is generally grey, or black, in colour, but when powdered it is cherry red. Magnetite (also an oxide of iron), another important ore, is the only mineral which is strongly attracted to a magnet. One form of magnetite, lodestone, is itself a natural magnet. The greatest haematite beds occur in the vicinity of Lake Superior, while enormous deposits of magnetite occur in northern Sweden. Less important ores of iron include limonite (hydrated oxide of iron) and siderite (iron carbonate).

Most of the iron produced nowadays is in the form of ferro alloys (an alloy is formed when one or more elements, usually metals, are added to the base metal). Steel is basically a mixture of iron and carbon (with between 0·1 and 1·6% of the latter). But many different types of steel are made to suit different purposes by adding small quantities of other metals such as tungsten, cobalt, nickel, molybdenum, vanadium, chromium and manganese. Tungsten steels, for instance, can withstand high temperatures and are widely used in high-speed cutting tools.

The chief ores of tungsten are scheelite and wolframite. Scheelite (calcium tungstate) is a glassy mineral, normally colourless, which usu-

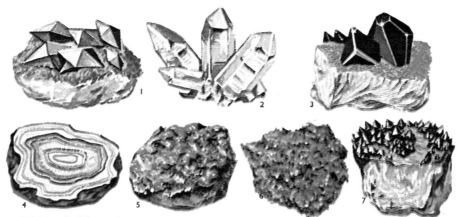

1. Mispickel (ore of arsenic) 2. Quartz 3. Tetrahedrite 4. Agate 5. Cinnabar 6. Native gold 7. Scheelite.

ally fluoresces under ultra-violet light. It is produced in large quantities in California and Nevada, U.S.A. Wolframite (a tungstate of iron and manganese) is a dark, brittle mineral, usually found in quartz veins, which occurs in large quantities in China and Burma.

Most of the world's cobalt is obtained from complex minerals which are often worked for the other metals they contain. At one time the chief source of this metal was cobaltite and smaltite occurring near Cobalt in Ontario, Canada, but now it is the copper mines of Katanga and Northern Rhodesia (Zambia). Cobalt 'bloom' describes the beautiful pinky-red colour which results from the weathering of cobalt minerals.

Chromium is used not only in various alloys such as stainless steels but also to provide a shining non-tarnish coating for less presentable metals. There is only one commercial ore of chromium—chromite (an oxide of iron and chromium). This is a brownish-black, brittle mineral associated with ultrabasic rocks. Leading producers include Turkey, South Africa and Rhodesia.

Manganese is extensively used to toughen steel and plays a vital part in the actual smelting process. The two chief ores are pyrolusite (manganese dioxide) and psilomelane (an impure hydrated oxide). Both are black in colour but psilomelane is much harder than pyrolusite. The principal manganese deposits are in the U.S.S.R. (around the Black Sea), India, South Africa and Ghana.

More than half of the nickel produced is used in the steel industry, particularly in the production of stainless steels. Pure nickel is also used for plating other metals since it is resistant to corrosion. Well over half of the world's production of nickel comes from the Sudbury region of Canada where pentlandite (a sulphide of iron and nickel) occurs in pyrrhotite (iron sulphide).

Molybdenum is extensively used in the manufacture of steels for aircraft and motor vehicles. Molybdenite, the chief ore, is a soft, brilliant, lead-grey mineral which occurs in vast deposits at Climax, Colorado, U.S.A.

The chief ores of vanadium, a metal which is being used in ever-increasing quantities in steels, are carnotite and vanadinite. The former is a complex mineral, canary-yellow in colour, and a source of uranium as well as vanadium. Vanadinite (vanadate and chloride of lead) is an attractive mineral ranging from ruby-red to yellow and brown in colour. It is a source of both vanadium and lead. The U.S.A. is by far the leading producer of vanadium.

Gold, the 'king of metals' and the basis of trade nearly everywhere, is one of the few metals which occur fairly frequently in the native state, i.e. uncombined with other elements (though in practice other metals, particularly silver, are usually present). Gold is found in quartz veins but as the deposits are eroded the heavy gold becomes concentrated in stream beds and can be recovered by washing away the lighter sand. It is also obtained from other minerals.

Like gold, silver occurs in the native state but in this case the chief source is the sulphide of the metal, argentite, a soft, shiny, lead-grey mineral often associated with native silver and galena. Galena (lead sulphide) is the chief ore of a much more common metal, humble lead. Another ore of lead is the pale grey, glistening cerussite (lead carbonate). South Africa and Mexico are the largest producers of gold and silver respectively while the U.S.A. and Australia head the long rank of lead producers.

Another metal often associated with lead is zinc. The chief ore is sphalerite (zinc sulphide). Sphalerite (meaning deceptive) is a good name for this mineral since its colour ranges from black to red, brown, green or yellow. The chief use of zinc is in providing a rust-proof coating on iron. The leading producers are the U.S.A. and Canada.

Aluminium is one of the most versatile metals. Being very light, non-corrosive and, in alloy form, as strong as steel, it is an ideal construction metal. Of the many aluminium minerals only bauxite (a mixture of hydrated aluminium oxides) is an ore of the metal. This is formed by the weathering of aluminium bearing rocks in a tropical climate. Though white by nature, the presence of iron gives it a reddish-brown colour. France was originally the leading producer of bauxite but this credit now goes to Dutch Guiana with British Guiana, Jamaica and the U.S.A. not far behind.

Another everyday metal is tin, 40% of which is used in providing an extremely thin protective layer on the iron of 'tin' cans. Like aluminium, tin has just one ore – cassiterite (oxide of tin). This brittle mineral is usually brown or black in colour and has a shiny lustre. Cassiterite occurs in alluvial deposits and in quartz veins. The leading producer of tin ore is Malaya, followed by Indonesia and Bolivia.

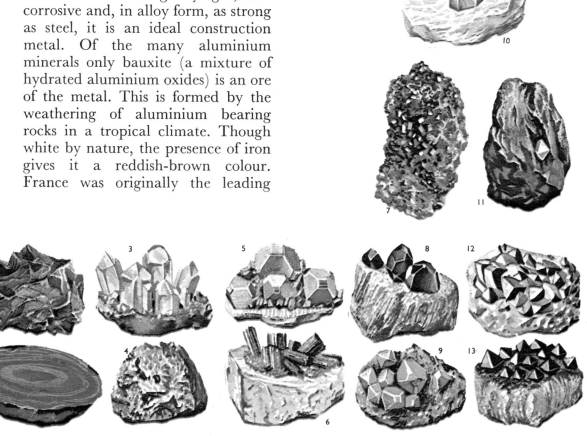

Opal 2. Jasper 3. Amethyst 4. Molybdenite 5. Galena 6. Manganite 7. Vanadinite 8. Haematite 9. Copper rite (chalcopyrite) 10. Corundum 11. Diamond 12. Smaltite 13. Magnetite.

Copper probably holds the distinction of being the first metal to be smelted from its ore by man. Today it is of paramount importance in the electrical industry, for it is an excellent conductor of electricity. Native copper does exist but the chief source of supply comes from the sulphides of the metal, chalcopyrite (a sulphide of copper and iron), chalcocite (cuprous sulphide) and bornite (sulphide of iron and copper). The copper minerals are notable for their magnificent colours, e.g. the vivid blue and green carbonates malachite and azurite. The U.S.A. is the chief producer of copper ore but large deposits occur in Chile, Zambia, U.S.S.R., Canada and Katanga.

This short selection of metals serves to show the tremendous importance of the metallic minerals in the service of man. But there are many non-metallic minerals which have a significant everyday value. Imagine, for instance, cooking without common salt (halite). This is just as much a mineral as any previously mentioned. So is graphite (carbon), which goes into the 'lead' of pencils, and asbestos (this is a loose term for a certain group of minerals of similar appearance), which is extensively used in fire-proof and heat-resistant materials.

Borax (sodium borate), formed by the evaporation of salt lakes, is an ore of boron widely used in the glass and ceramic industries. Sulphur occurs as the native element as a result of volcanic activity. Its chief use is in the manufacture of sulphuric acid.

Coal and petroleum are not true minerals, for their origin is organic. There are also a number of rocks of commercial importance, e.g. chalk used in the manufacture of cement.

Index

Acidic magmas, 113, 114
Aerial photographs, 23
Agate, 122, 123
Albite, crystal of, 116
Alpine orogenisis, 58
Aluminium, 125
Amethyst, 122, 125
Andesite, 35
Anglesite, 117
Anthracite, 101
Anticline, 38
Apatite, 118
  crystal of, 117
Aragonite, 33
  crystal of, 116
Arch, natural, 83
Arenaceous deposits, 29
Arête, 80, 81
Argentite, 124
Argillaceous deposits, 30
Asbestos, 126
Attrition, 87
Augite, crystal of, 117
Axinite, crystal of, 116
Azurite, 117, 126

Barchans, 84, 85
Basalt, 6, 35
Basal till, 82
Basic magma, 113
Bathyliths, 36
Bauxite, 125
Beaches, 89, 90
Bedding planes, 91
Bergshrund, 80
Beryl, 123
Bituminous coal, 101, 102
Borax, 117, 126
Bornite, 117, 126
Boulder clay, 81, 82
Breccias, 29
Brown coal, 10
Brown forest earth, 46

Cairngorm, 122
Calcite, 118
Caledonian front, 59
Cambrian period, 17
Carboniferous period, 17, 101
Carnotite, 124
Cassiterite, 118, 125
Caves, 91–94
Celestite, 117, 122
Cenozoic era, 17
Cerussite, 125
Chabazite, 117
Chalcopyrite, 117, 125, 126
Chalk, 32, 126
Cheddar Gorge, 91
Chemical weathering, 69
Chernosem, 46
Chromite, 119, 124
Chromium, 124
Chrysoberyl, crystal of, 116
Chrysotile, 120, 121
Cinnabar, 123
Citrine, 122
Clastic deposits, 28–30
Clays, 30
Cleavage of minerals, 121
Cliffs, 87, 88
Clinometer, 22, 23
Coal, 100–103
Coal measures, 102, 103
Coasts, Atlantic, 85
  Pacific, 85

Cobalt, 124
Cobalt bloom, 124
Cobaltite, 124
Colour of minerals,`120
Conglomerates, 28, 29
Continental drift, 58–64
Copper, 126
  native, 122
Core of Earth, 7, 10, 11
Corrasion, 73, 87
Corrie, 81
Corrosion, 73, 87
Corundum, 118, 120, 125
Cretaceous period, 17
Crinoidal limestone, 32, 33
Cross-bedding, 16
Cross-profile of river valleys, 76, 77
Crust of Earth, 6–14
Crystallography, 116–118
Current-bedding, 16

Denudation, 70
Devonian period, 17
Diachronism, 16
Diamond, 118, 119, 122, 125
Dolerite, 35
Dolomite, 32
Drumlins, 82
Dunite, 35
Dust bowl, 70
Dyke, 49
Dynamic metamorphism, 37

Earth, history of, 14–26
  origin of, 18, 19
  structure of, 6–14
Earth pillars, 71
Earthquakes, 51–53
Emerald, 123
Emergent coasts, 85
Epicentre (of earthquake), 51
Erosion, 70–94
  agents of, 70–93
  by moving ice, 79–83
  by running water, 73–79
  by the sea, 85–90
  by the wind, 83–90
Erratics, 82
Eskers, 82
Exfoliation, 68
Extrusive rocks, 34

Fan folds, 39, 40
Faults, 41, 91
Felsite, 35
Felspars, 29, 30, 69
Ferro-alloys, 123
Fiords, 80, 81
Fissure eruptions, 51
Flame tests, 117
Flood plains, 76, 77
Fluorite, 120
  crystal of, 116
Fluorspar, 118
Folding, types of, 38–40
Fool's gold, 118
Fossils, 15–17, 100
Fracture of minerals, 121
Fragmental rocks, 28–30
Frost shattering, 66, 68

Gabbros, 35, 36
Galena, 118, 121, 124, 125
Ganister, 103
Garnet, 120
Geological column, 15

Geological map,
  construction of, 21–24
Geological time scale, 17
  calibrating the, 18
Geologist, work of, 21–26
Geology, applications of, 24, 25
Geosyncline, 55–58
  formation of, 55
Geothermal heat, 106–111
Geysers, 106–108
Giant's Causeway, 50, 51
Glacial deposition, 81, 82
  erosion, 79–81
Glaciers, 79–83
Glauberite, 117
Gneiss, 37
Gold, 124
  crystal of, 116
  native, 123
Gondwanaland, 59
Gorges, 75, 77
Graded bedding, 16
Grading of rivers, 75–79
Granite, 6, 34–6
Graphite, 122, 126
Gravel beds, 84
Gravimetric survey, 26, 100
Great Ice Age, 79
Ground-water, 73
Gypsum, 118

Haematite, 119, 120, 123, 125
Halite, 117, 126
Hanging valleys, 80, 81
Hercynian front, 59
Hexagonal crystals, 116
Hornfels, 37
Hot springs, 106, 107
Hutton, James, 14, 17
Hypabyssal rocks, 35, 36

Igneous ores, 112–114
Igneous rocks, 34–36
  classification of, 35
Ilmenite, 119
Intrusive rocks, 35
Iron, 123
Iron pyrites, 118
Isoclinal folds, 39, 40
Isometric crystals, 116
Isoseimals, 51
Isostasy, 54, 56

Jaspar, 122, 125
Joints, 91
Jurassic period, 17
Juvenile water, 108

Kaolinite, 120

Laccoliths, 35, 36, 49
Lateral moraines, 80, 82
Laterite, 46
Laurasia, 59
Lava, 49, 50
Lazurite, 117
Lead, 124, 125
Lignite, 101
Limburgite, 35
Limestone, 32, 33
  caves in, 92–94
  scarp, 94
Limonite, 123
Lithology, 16
Lodestone, 119, 123
Loess, 30, 83

Longshore drift 87, 89, 90
Lopolith, 35
Lustre of minerals, 120

Mafe, 10
Magma, 36, 49
Magnetic survey, 26, 100
Magnetite, 119, 123, 125
Malachite, 117, 122, 126
Mammoth Hole system, 93
Manganese, 124
Manganite, 125
Mantle of Earth, 7–14
Marble, 37
Marine deposition, 89, 90
  erosion, 85–89
Meanders, 77, 79
Mechanical weathering, 66–68
Medial moraines, 80, 82
Mercalli scale, 51, 53
Mesozoic era, 17
Metals, 112–126
Metamorphic ores, 113, 114
  rocks, 36, 37
Metamorphism, 36, 37
Meteoric water, 108
Mica, 120, 121
  schist, 34
Minerals, 112–126
  commercially important, 121–126
  identification of, 116–121
  prospecting for, 115
Mispickel, 123
Mississippian period, 17
Mohole project, 11–14
Mohorovičić discontinuity, 8, 9, 10
Mohs' scale of hardness, 118, 119
Molybdenite, 124, 125
Molybdenum, 124
Monoclinic crystals, 116
Moraines, 80, 82
Mountain building, 54–58
Muscovite, 119

Natural gas, 104, 105
Nickel, 124

Obsidian, 35
Oil geology, 96–100
  traps, 98
Oligoclase, 117
Onyx, 122
Oolites, 33
Opal, 122, 125
Ordovician period, 17
Orogenic cycle, 54–56, 57
Orthoclase, 118, 119
Orthorhombic crystals, 116
Outwash fans, 83
Overfolding, 15, 16

Palaeogeography, 15
Palaeozoic era, 17
Pangaea, 62, 64
Peat, 100
Peneplain, 79
Pennsylvanian period, 17, 101
Pentlandite, 124

Peridotite, 10, 35
Permian period, 17
Phreatic zone, 93
Pisolites, 33
Placer deposits, 113
Platinum, 119
Plutonic rocks, 35, 36
Podsols, 44, 45
Porosity, 91
Pot-holes, 93
Psilomelane, 122, 124
Pumice stone, 34
Pyrite crystal, 116
Pyroclasts, 50
Pyrolusite, 124
Pyrrhotite, 119, 124

Quartz, 118, 120, 121, 123
  porphyry, 35
Quaternary period, 17

Raised beaches, 85
Realgar, crystal of, 117
Recumbent folds, 39
Regional metamorphism, 37
Rendzinas, 44
Reverse faults, 41
Rhodonite, crystal of, 116
Rhyolite, 35
Rivers, 73–79
  erosion by, 73–79
  rejuvenation of, 79
  terraces, 79
  transport by, 74, 75
  life history of, 75–79
Rock crystal, 121
Rock flour, 82
Rocks, sedimentary, 28–33
  igneous and metamorphic, 34–37
Rose quartz, 122
Ruby, 120, 123
Rudaceous deposits, 29

Sand dunes, 84, 85
Sapphire, 123
Sard, 122
Scapolite, crystal of, 117
Scheelite, 123
Scree, 66, 67
Sea caves, 91, 92
  stacks, 87
Sedimentary ores, 114, 115
Sedimentary rocks, 28–33
Seismic survey, 96
  waves, 7–10, 52, 53
Seismograms, 7–11
Seismographs, 52
Shadow zone, 7
Shakeholes, 91,93
Sial, 6
Sidenite, 123
Silica, 35, 121
Sill, 49
Silurian period, 17
Silver, 124
Sima, 6
Sink holes, 93
Slate, 37

Smaltite, 124, 125
Smith, William, 15
Snider, Antonio, 58
Soil erosion, 68
Soils, 41–46
  composition of, 42, 43
  texture of, 43, 44
  types of, 44–46
Specific gravity of minerals, 118
Sphalerite, 124
Spits, 90
Stalactites, 33, 94
Stalagmites, 33, 94
Staurolite, crystal of, 116
Stibnite, 119
Storm beaches, 89
Stratigraphy, 15
Streak of minerals, 120
Strontianite, 117
Submergent coasts, 85
Sulphur, 118, 120, 126
Superglacial till, 82
Superposition, law of, 15
Swallow holes, 93
Syenite, 35
Syncline, 38

Talc, 118, 120
Taylor, F. B., 59
Tear fault, 41
Terminal moraines, 82
Tertiary period, 17
Tethys, 62
Tetragonal crystals, 116
Tetrahedrite, 117, 123
Thermal metamorphism, 37
Thrusts, 41
Tin, 125
Topaz, 118
Tourmaline, 120
Triassic period, 17
Triclinic crystals, 116
Tungsten, 123

Ultra-basic rocks, 10
Ultra-metamorphism, 37
Unconformities, 14, 15

Vadose zone, 93
Vanadinite, 124, 125
Vanadium, 124
Volcanic plugs, 51
  rocks, 35
Volcanoes, 48–51
  diagrammatic structure of, 48

Wairakei project, 107–111
Waterfalls, 78, 79
Wave action, 85–87
Wave-cut platforms, 88
Weathering, 66–69
Wegener, Alfred, 61–64
Wind erosion, 83–85
Wolframite, 122–124

Zincite, crystal of, 117
Zircon crystal, 117